HANDBOOK
OF
LIVESTOCK EQUIPMENT

HANDBOOK
OF
LIVESTOCK EQUIPMENT

by

ELWOOD M. JUERGENSON, Ph.D.

Professor of Agricultural Education
Teacher Educator—Agriculture
Department of Applied Behavioral Sciences
University of California, Davis

THE INTERSTATE
Printers & Publishers, Inc.

Danville, Illinois

Library of Congress Catalog Card No. 72-144080

PRINTED IN U.S.A.

PREFACE

The science of livestock production has advanced so far that quality milk, meat, and meat products at reasonable prices are expected and taken for granted. Over the years most effort has centered around unraveling the biological mysteries of livestock production. Great strides in genetics, nutrition, disease prevention and control, parasitology, physiology, and other segments of biology have produced better livestock and livestock products at a lower cost in a shorter period. While the science and technology of livestock production have advanced, much of the manual, on-the-farm, day-by-day operation of livestock production has lagged behind.

In order for livestock production to be efficient, equipment and labor-saving devices must also be devised capable of doing the job of assisting in livestock management and putting into actions the decisions of management efficiently and rapidly.

While a great deal of science may be involved in decision making in livestock production, a large amount of equipment is employed in putting to use the decisions and know-how of science. Furthermore, while the time spent in decision making may be very small, even though most important, the time spent in carrying out the decisions may be very great. A rancher may spend an hour, or sometimes only a few minutes, making an important decision regarding the management of his operations, but he can take hours, or even days, in putting this decision into action.

Much equipment and proper facilities are needed in order for livestock production to be efficient. The high cost of labor in the modern agricultural world makes this factor even more significant. Efficiency of production depends on efficient equipment and facilities, especially if viewed in the knowledge that most of the time a livestock producer spends is in working with equipment.

The aim of this book is to bring together most of the information known about equipment and facilities that have to do with efficient livestock production. Safety and labor-saving equipment have been highlighted throughout the volume, as well as the use of local economical resource material.

In numerous instances more than one set of plans are shown for a given item. This is done purposely so producers, teachers, or students may have a choice that fits their individual preference, available materials, or ranch conditions. With few exceptions enough detail is shown and enough sizes are indicated so that anyone who is handy with tools and who has some knowledge of construction can build the equipment directly from drawings in the book.

Livestock producers, teachers, extension workers or county agents, students, 4H, and FFA will find a wealth of ideas in this publication needed to put the science of livestock production into action.

ACKNOWLEDGMENTS

Some of the plans in this book are original; many are not. However, every effort has been made to credit the proper source, for several obvious reasons. First, courtesy demands that recognition be given to the originator. Second, in many cases you may wish to know where to turn to receive additional information concerning the drawings and plans, so a credit source readily provides this opportunity.

A prime source of information has been the many state universities and branches of USDA. Special thanks go to the American Hereford Association for allowing the use of drawings from their publication "Equipment for the Hereford Producer."

The following state universities and experiment stations provide a wealth of desirable plans and suggestions:

Alabama	Nevada
California	New York
Colorado	Oklahoma
Florida	Oregon
Illinois	Pennsylvania
Kansas	Texas
Kentucky	Washington
Missouri	Wyoming
Montana	

All of the original plans and sketches were done by Don M. Juergenson, Auburn, California. The writer is extremely grateful for the help and talent in providing these original works.

TABLE OF CONTENTS

Chapter I

BUILDINGS AND SHELTER FOR LIVESTOCK

The agricultural revolution of the last half century has produced incredible advances and changes in the production of food and fiber. Traditional methods and ideas in livestock production are no exception to the rule of doing things in better ways. One important change has been the shift in value of investment from real estate to livestock and equipment. Historically, land has always accounted for the greatest single investment in agricultural production. However, today there are many progressive persons in production agriculture who have considerably more invested in equipment and livestock than they have in land. True, land or real estate is still the basis for all production, and especially so in the livestock industry. Nevertheless, the importance of buildings and equipment is constantly increasing, particularly when viewed from the standpoint of efficiency in production.

Buildings and Shelter for Livestock

The activities of a livestock enterprise center around the buildings, and around the people that guide its operation. The popular concept is that buildings and shelters are made primarily for the comfort of animals. While this idea is, in many cases, based on fact, a truer picture is that buildings and equipment are designed for the comfort, efficiency, and safety of the operator. Feeders are designed to save feed, milking parlors to produce clean milk with a minimum of labor, and restraining equipment to protect the operator and animal in addition to providing an efficient method of performing an operation. So, in most cases, the needs of the operator are foremost, rather than the needs of the livestock involved. Shelters do protect livestock from severe winter weather, as do sun shades from summer heat; but, given a choice, most animals prefer to stay outside in the open, especially if the terrain provides natural areas of comfort.

A second consideration is that livestock producers must always be profit-minded. Barns that store feed, feeders that save feed, fences that maintain livestock, cattle guards that save time, squeeze chutes that protect life, and buildings that provide comfort, especially for the operator, are all part of the investment each livestock producer is concerned about. If the comfort and efficiency of the operator is of paramount concern, it is fitting that the first plans in this book have to do with the entire farmstead.

1

Planning the Farmstead

Adequate total planning will pay big dividends, whether a total new farmstead or headquarters is involved or an existing one is being revamped. To do less means a "tacked-on," junky appearance that, in most cases, is very inefficient. Even landscaping should be a result of total planning, with the final outcome detailed in advance to avoid overplanting, and the costly removal and rearrangement of trees and other plants at a later date.

The Washington State Extension Service has some excellent directions in Bulletin 467 regarding the development of a planned farmstead.

A Good Farmstead Plan Pays Dividends

The farmstead is the family "home site" and the home base for all farm operations. It is the storage plant, processing plant, and distribution point for all farm products. A well-organized farmstead contributes much to farm living and makes all farm work easier.

Each farmstead is an individual problem. Generally, a good arrangement is not difficult to obtain because individual characteristics suggest one. For instance, unusual contours often require special placing of lanes. These in turn suggest a farmstead arrangement to fit.

Sound farmstead arrangement ideas are just as important to the family with an existing farmstead as they are for the family who must start with raw land. In either case, you must know where you are going. How else will you get there?

In a majority of cases you will not be able to build new. Some buildings, corrals, fences, or areas may already exist and be in use. So, you may think "there is little I can do to better my arrangement." That is not true. Farm people are constantly changing things—remodeling, rebuilding—to meet changing conditions and desires.

A good plan clearly defined and kept in mind is as valuable for the family on an existing farm as for the family who builds new. An excellent method is to forget, for a time, your present farmstead. Do a new arrangement—one that you would like if you could do it all over. You will be surprised at the resulting plan and at how many of your existing structures fit. But more important, this method clarifies your objectives as nothing else can.

First Locate the Farmstead

The first move is to locate the best place for your farmstead. Until the location is settled, there is little point in doing a layout for it. The reason—a change in location in almost every case completely changes the arrangement.

There is probably more than one possible location for it. Consider each—then choose the one that has the most advantages.

Here are some points to think about: The farmstead is a natural control center. Place it near a road or highway so it is convenient to mail service, the school bus, and power and telephone lines.

If you stay near the road you avoid long driveways and the extra maintenance necessary for them. On the other hand, if your farm is on the downwind side of an unpaved highway, it may be wise to plan to locate the farmstead far enough away to keep out of dust clouds.

In some areas where winter winds and drifting snow are a problem, consider existing natural windbreaks. Clumps of trees or hills may save you money.

It is not always possible to take advantage of all these factors. Only you can decide which is important in your case.

Once the site is fixed you are ready to plan its arrangement.

The final location of the drive and parking area is not determined until the house plan is finished. In any case, place them near the front door so guests don't park in the farm court. Mrs. Farmer doesn't like her guests to come in through the back door.

When you spot the power pole, choose a location out of traffic lanes. Locate this pole near the building or group of buildings with the greatest power demand. In most cases, the farm shop, the farmhouse, and the well use most of the electricity. The milk house and poultry house are sometimes big users of electrical power.

Place buildings you use together near each other. Such buildings as feed barns, feed storage, silo, milk house, milking parlors, and corrals are usually used as a unit. Spread these buildings apart and you increase your daily travel.

For appearance it is best to locate open-type buildings, like the machine shed, to face away from the highway. Find a place for an outdoor parking area for machinery back of a building or clump of trees. Areas like this are usually cluttered, and their appearance from the highway is not good.

Important Points to Remember

LOCATE YOUR FARMSTEAD—

1. **Near a highway because of mail, school bus, power lines, telephone, and access.**
2. **At a natural farm control center.**
3. **Near an available domestic water supply.**
4. **Near irrigation turnout.**
5. **On good soil for lawn and garden.**
6. **To take advantage of the view.**

ARRANGE YOUR FARMSTEAD SO—

1. **The house is nearest the road and upwind from farm buildings.**
2. **All buildings and corrals border the court.**
3. **The garden is near the house.**
4. **The drainage is away from the house and well.**
5. **It is easy to use and maintain.**

Pole-Type Buildings

The construction and use of pole-type buildings has increased steadily in recent years. W. S. Allen, Extension Agricultural Engineer, Texas A & M University, explains in Publication MP-638 that most farm operators find that pole-type buildings fulfill many requirements satisfactorily and usually cost less than other conventional structures of wood. With proper design and certain construction methods, much of the usual cutting of framing members can be eliminated. Simple lapping of standard lengths of lumber at joints reduces the necessity for most special cuts except for the roof framing or a few special joints. Many designs of pole-type construction are likely to be found among standard construction plans from different sources. Follow any plan you select closely. Changing the designer's methods of framing, size of members, and special construction details may result in weakening of the building.

In Oregon State Experiment Station Bulletin 557, Leroy Bonnicksen comments on multicombination pole-type construction.

Round Poles

Round poles are purchased by top diameter and length, including the part that is placed in the ground. All poles to which 2 x 12 rafters are attached should have at least 5-inch top diameters, and poles on which trusses are attached should have at least 6-inch top diameters. Larger-diameter poles can be used if you can obtain them for little or no additional cost.

Square Posts

Square-sawed timber posts can be used instead of poles. A 6 x 6 post should work satisfactorily for any length up to 20 feet. Use an 8 x 8 if lengths are more than 20 feet. Square posts should be incised (have holes punched into the sides) before treating.

Preservative Treatment

Maximum useful life of poles can be obtained and expensive repairs avoided by using only wood that has been treated in conformity with the standards of the American Wood Preservers Association. These standards allow cedar poles to be treated by the hot-cold-bath method while pressure treatment is required for all other pole species. Properly treated poles will contain numerous seasoning cracks and will be penetrated by the preservative for a depth of ½ to 1½ inches or more from the surface, depending on the species being treated. Deeper penetrations are usually more necessary in warm, humid regions than in cold, dry regions where decay conditions are much less severe. Treated wood can be obtained from commercial treating plants or their distributors. **Home treatments seldom provide adequate protection for building poles.**

Depth

How deep you sink a pole determines its rigidity, and therefore its ability to resist wind and lateral loads. Pole-type construction utilizes rigidity in eliminating or reducing the bracing normally required with other types of construction. Therefore it is very important that you follow the recommendations for depth given.

DEPTH OF POLE

Pole Length	Soft Soils	Ordinary and Firm Soils
	(ft.)	(ft.)
Up to 16 feet	4½	4 (minimum depth)
Up to 20 feet	5	4½
Up to 25 feet	5½	5
Up to 30 feet	6	5½

Footings

With pole-type construction each pole will support a heavy, concentrated load. Under most soil conditions, this load is heavy enough to cause the poles to settle.

Since such settling is not good, footings are used.

Two types of footings are recommended—the concrete type and the gravel type. Gravel footing can be unwashed, pit-run gravel, well proportioned with fine, medium, and coarse-size particles.

Footings are put in the bottom of the hole, which is dug deeper than the depth of the pole. The minimum-footing diameter chart gives the minimum recommended footing diameters for the type of construction and type of soil. Usually, the diameter of the hole necessary to set the pole easily in the ground is enough for the diameter of the footing. In some cases, where the diameter of the hole is smaller than the required diameter of the footing, the hole can be widened at the lower end for the footing. The bottom of the hole can be rounded and does not need to be level.

After the footings have been put in place, the poles can be placed in the holes and aligned. The poles are located at ground level by placing a chalk line or stretching a string along one side of the poles and by measuring from the outside edge of the end pole to the center of the inner poles. The vertical alignment or the location of the tops of the poles is done by sighting through two plumb bobs. These plumb bobs should be at right angles to each other. The poles can be held in place by braces nailed to stakes or by three pike poles.

When the poles are aligned and held in place, the holes should be partially backfilled. The backfilling can be finished when the roof frame has been attached, squared, and the building temporarily braced against further movement during assembly.

MINIMUM FOOTING DIAMETER

Type of Construction	Soft Soils (Soft clay, sandy loam, or silt)	Ordinary Soils (Ordinary clay and sand)	Firm Soils (Dry, hard clay [hardpan]; coarse, firm sand, gravel or rock)
	(in.)	(in.)	
All poles on which only 2 x 12 rafters are mounted, and 16-foot poles on which 24-foot trussed rafters are mounted..................	28	16	No footing necessary
20-foot or longer poles on which 24-foot trussed rafters are mounted	34	20	No footing necessary

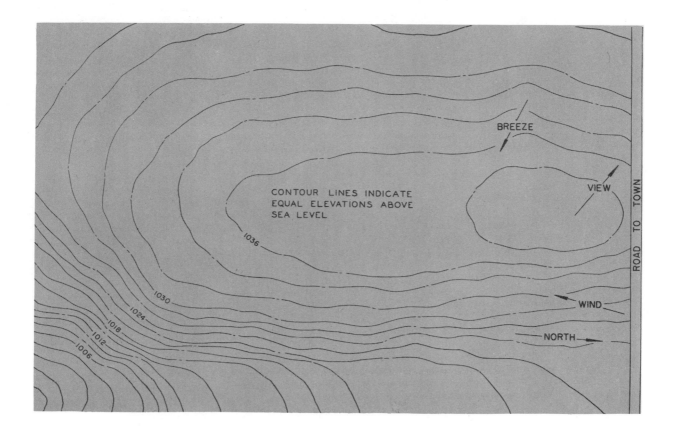

Contour map.

The use of a contour map enables the planner to locate the farm house and other buildings to best advantage. It is important to locate buildings, fences, and gates in proper relationship to each other, in order to save labor and energy, and to provide the best view and shelter from winds and odors.

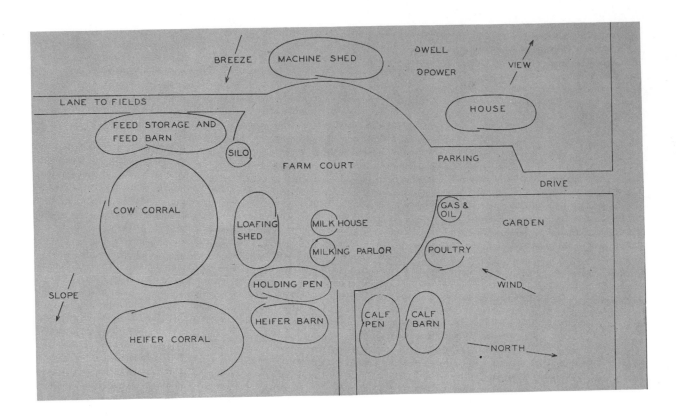

Completed farmstead building arrangement.

The milk house is near the drive and farm house and convenient for the milk truck.

Next to the milk house is the milking parlor. It is connected to the loafing shed and corral by the holding pen.

The loafing shed, while not connected to the feed barn, is near at hand. It is on the farm court, and machinery can enter it easily.

Near the lane that runs to the forage fields are the feed storage and silo. This makes feed storage easier and faster.

The barn for the heifers has its own feed storage, and access to this building is easy from the court.

This arrangement fits the conditions and requirements of this farm. It fits this farm but it probably will not fit any other layout. If any one factor is changed the whole arrangement changes.

You are the only one who can make the necessary decisions that go into your plan arrangement. You know your work habits and desires.

Oil and gas storage is near the house, available from the farm court and screened from the living area and the road.

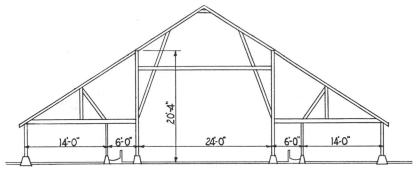

Gable-roof barn showing hay storage manger locations.

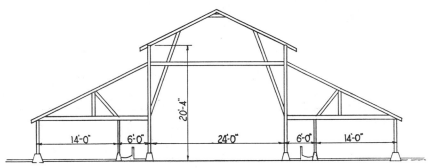

Feed and shelter barn with monitor roof.

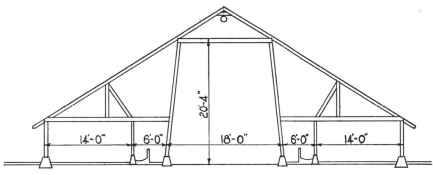

A feed and shelter barn especially designed for chopped hay. Sloping the side posts along mow
relieves them of pressure when the hay settles.

Cross section of three different types of barns for livestock and hay storage.

CAPACITY PER FOOT OF BARN LENGTH

	U.C. Barn Plan No.		
	136	137	225
Volume (cu. ft./ft. of barn length)	480	480	512
Capacity (ton/ft. of barn length)			
Long hay	1.0	1.0	1.0
Baled hay	2.5	2.5	2.5
Chopped hay	2.8	2.8	3.0

(University of California Circular 414)

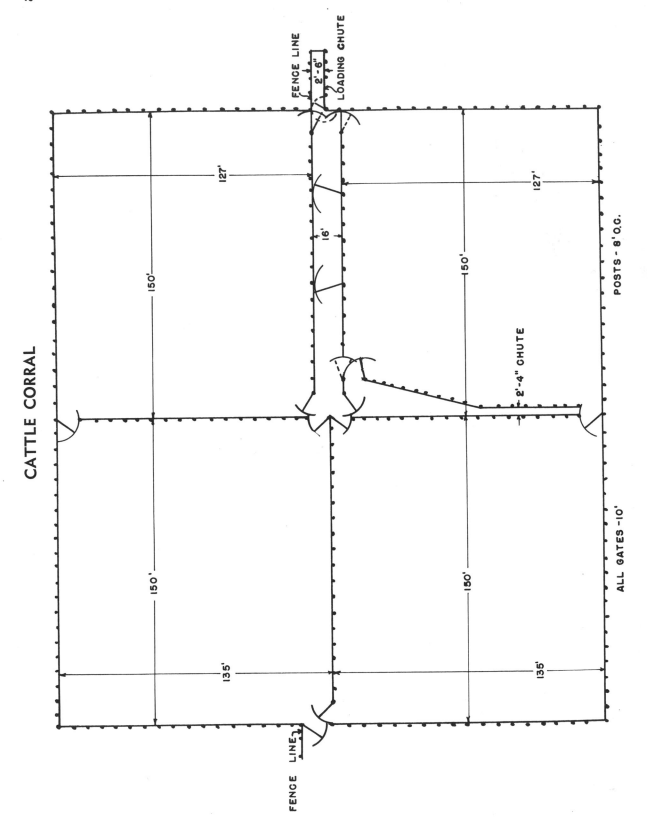

CATTLE CORRAL

FENCE LINE

2'-6"

LOADING CHUTE

127'

127'

16'

150'

150'

150'

2'-4" CHUTE

POSTS - 8' O.C.

150'

150'

135'

135'

ALL GATES -10'

FENCE LINE

Cattle corral.

This cattle corral is designed to handle several hundred head of cattle. Pens are arranged around a control point for diverting livestock to any one of four pens or to loading or restraining chutes.

Posts should be decay-resistant and should be set 6 to 8 feet apart and 2½ feet into the ground. Corner posts should be set 3 to 4 feet into the ground. Set posts on outside of corral fence, and round the corners or pad them. (University of Wyoming Circular 148)

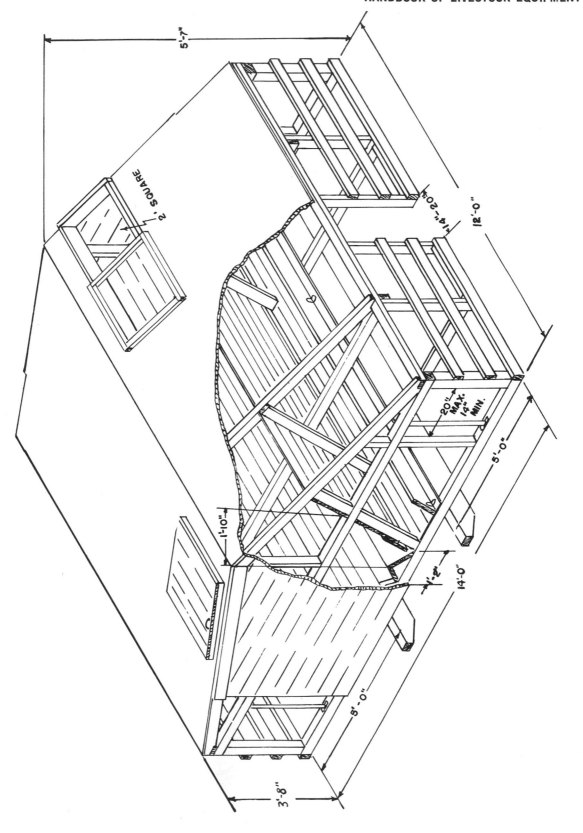

Cutaway pictorial view of creep feeder with built-in fence.

Calves also are given some shade and protection while eating. The self-feeder is portable, so it can be placed near the water supply or other places where cattle tend to gather. It is designed to eliminate the cross braces which the calves must cross over, unless they back out. (University of Wyoming Circular 148—Plan No. FE 16)

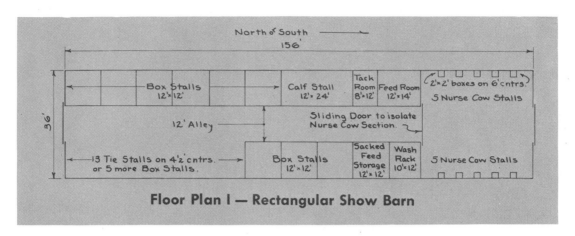

Floor Plan I — Rectangular Show Barn

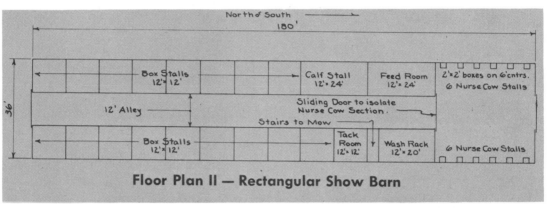

Floor Plan II — Rectangular Show Barn

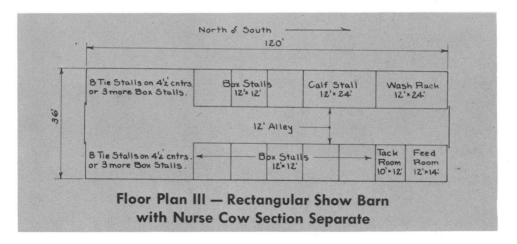

**Floor Plan III — Rectangular Show Barn
with Nurse Cow Section Separate**

Three show barn plans.

The show barn should be planned in units of 12 feet and the nurse cow section in units of 6 feet, with a 12-foot alley throughout. There should be an earthen floor in the stalls and alley, a concrete floor in the wash rack, and in the storage, feed, and tack rooms, and a sand floor in the nurse cow section. The storage room should be built so that it can become a part of the wash rack when the herd grows and the need for a larger rack arises. (American Hereford Association)

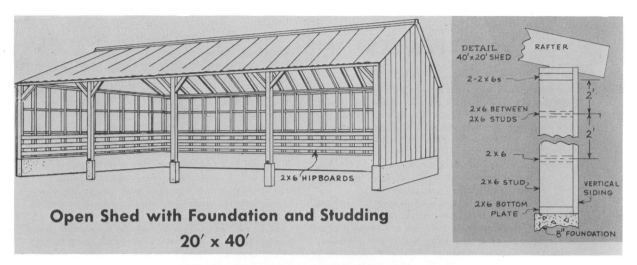

Open Shed with Foundation and Studding
20' x 40'

DETAIL
40'x20' SHED

RAFTER

2-2x6s

2x6 BETWEEN
2x6 STUDS

2x6

2x6 STUD

2x6 BOTTOM
PLATE

VERTICAL
SIDING

8" FOUNDATION

2x6 HIP BOARDS

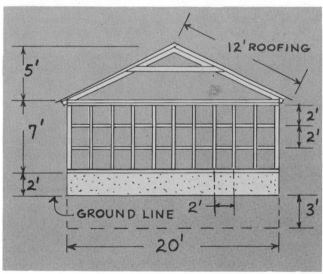

12' ROOFING

5'

7'

2'

GROUND LINE

2'

2'

2'

3'

20'

An open shed, built with a foundation and studding.

This is one of two general types of open, or three-sided, sheds (see also the following illustration). It is a practical shed on a concrete block foundation. The sides and roof are of corrugated iron, and the heavy widespread studs are well braced. In the opinion of many breeders, sheds of this type should be approximately 9 feet to the eaves.

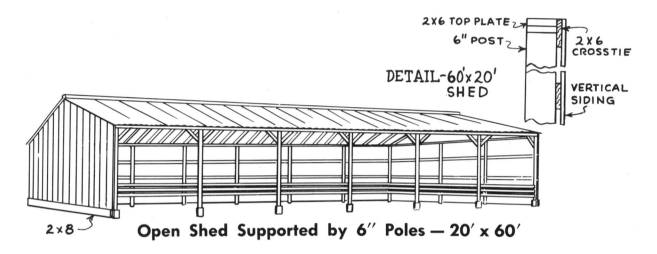

2X6 TOP PLATE

6" POST

2X6 CROSSTIE

DETAIL-60'x20' SHED

VERTICAL SIDING

Open Shed Supported by 6" Poles — 20' x 60'

2×8

Pole type of open shed.

This attractive shed is 10 feet to the eaves, with the front dropped 2 feet. An advantage of the pole type is the removable 2 x 8 around the bottom. The siding is not attached to this 2 x 8, so the latter can be replaced as it decays and the siding left undisturbed.

Sheds should be faced so that the solid end is toward storms or prevailing winds. If possible the open end should be placed so visitors do not look directly into the clutter of machinery. Open sheds such as this and the one shown in the preceding illustration can be used for either livestock or implements, or for a combination of both.

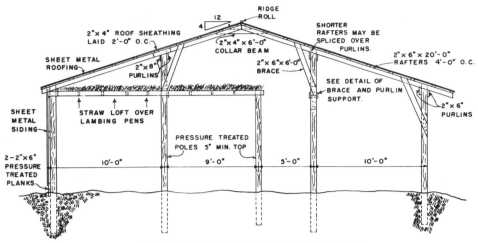

SECTION SHOWING INTERIOR FRAMING

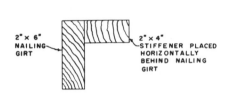

SECTION THROUGH NAILING GIRT
DETAIL A A

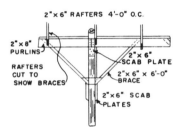

BRACES AND PURLIN
SUPPORTS AT CENTER POLES

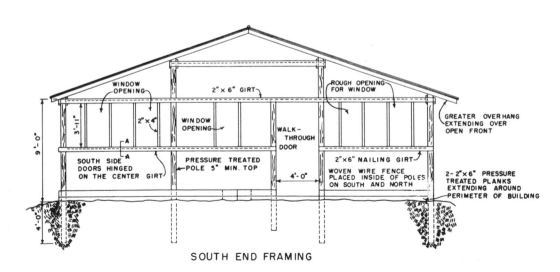

SOUTH END FRAMING

Simple low-cost sheep barn.

These end-framing and cross-section views of a sheep barn show the details of the construction. (University of Missouri Bulletin 655)

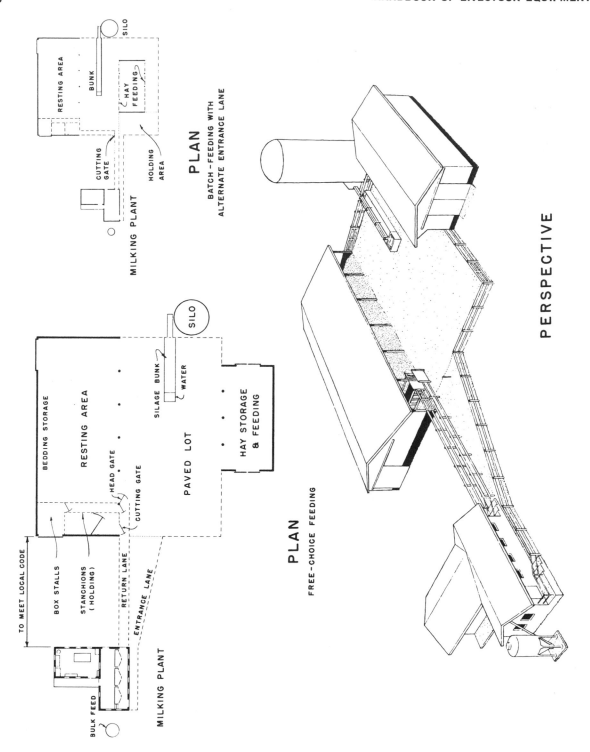

Loose housing layout.

This attractive dairy layout should be checked against local codes. (Cooperative Extension, Texas A & M University—Plan 5882)

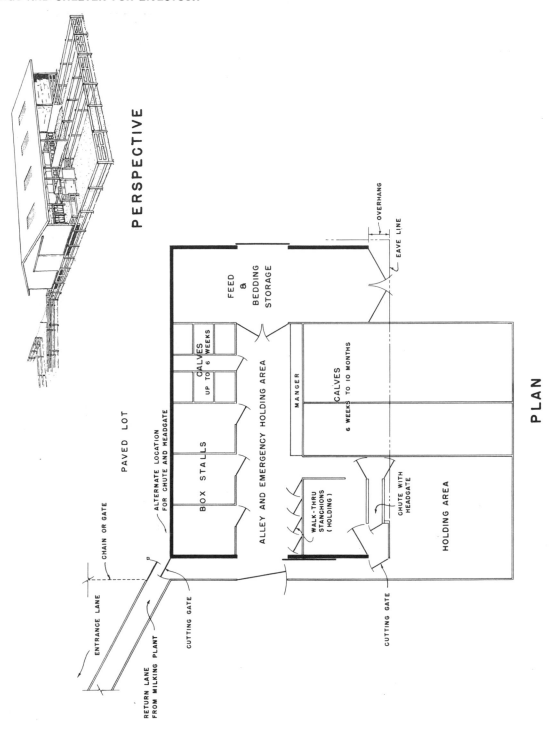

Calf and maternity building.

This facility is designed for the ease and comfort of the operator as well as the safety and function of the livestock. (Cooperative Extension, Texas A & M University—Plan 5898)

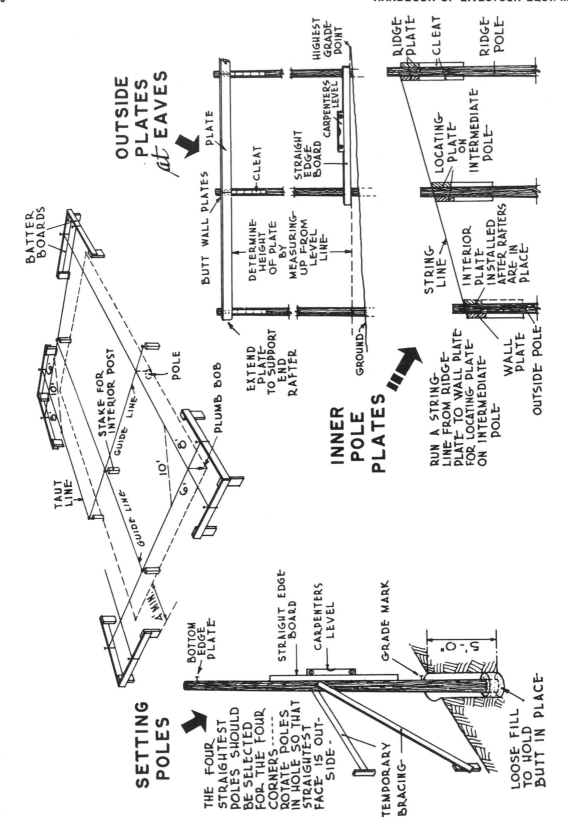

Building layout.

The site should be graded so all drainage is away from the building.

Square the corners, using a triangle with sides of 6, 8, and 10 feet (or any multiple of 3, 4, and 5 feet). The diagonal measurements are equal if the building is square. (Cooperative Extension, Texas A & M University—MP-638)

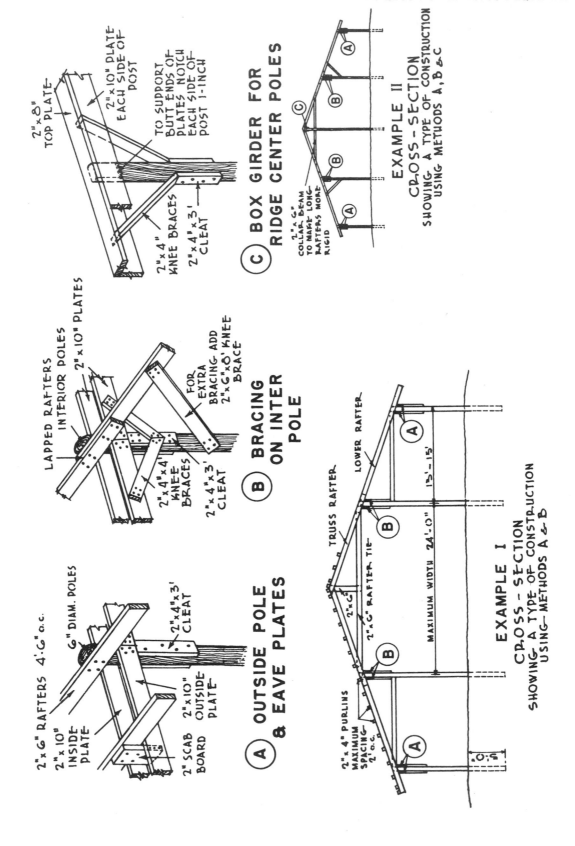

C BOX GIRDER FOR RIDGE CENTER POLES

2"×8" TOP PLATE
2"×10" PLATE EACH SIDE OF POST
TO SUPPORT BUTT ENDS OF PLATES NOTCH EACH SIDE OF POST 1-INCH
2"×4" KNEE BRACES
2"×4"×3' CLEAT

2"×6" COLLAR BEAM TO MAKE LONG RAFTERS MORE RIGID

EXAMPLE II
CROSS-SECTION
SHOWING A TYPE OF CONSTRUCTION USING METHODS A, B & C

B BRACING ON INTER POLE

LAPPED RAFTERS INTERIOR POLES
2"×10" PLATES
FOR EXTRA BRACING ADD 2"×6"×6' KNEE BRACE
2"×4"×4" KNEE BRACES
2"×4"×3' CLEAT

A OUTSIDE POLE & EAVE PLATES

2"×6" RAFTERS 4'6" o.c.
6" DIAM. POLES
2"×4"×3' CLEAT
2"×10" INSIDE PLATE
2" SCAB BOARD
2"×10" OUTSIDE PLATE

LOWER RAFTER
TRUSS RAFTER
2"×6" RAFTER TIE
2"×6"
MAXIMUM WIDTH 24'-0"
15'-15'
2"×4" PURLINS MAXIMUM SPACING 2' o.c.
5'-0"

EXAMPLE I
CROSS-SECTION
SHOWING A TYPE OF CONSTRUCTION USING METHODS A & B

Typical pole-type construction details.

Using preservative-treated poles with a minimum of 6-inch-diameter top, using 2" x 10" or 2" x 12" plates running lengthwise of the building, and 2" x 6" rafters placed 2'-0" to 4'-6" o.c.

Caution: Purlins for roofing should be spaced at a maximum of 24 inches o.c. This spacing is for .024-inch aluminum or 28-gauge steel. (Cooperative Extension, Texas A & M University—MP-638)

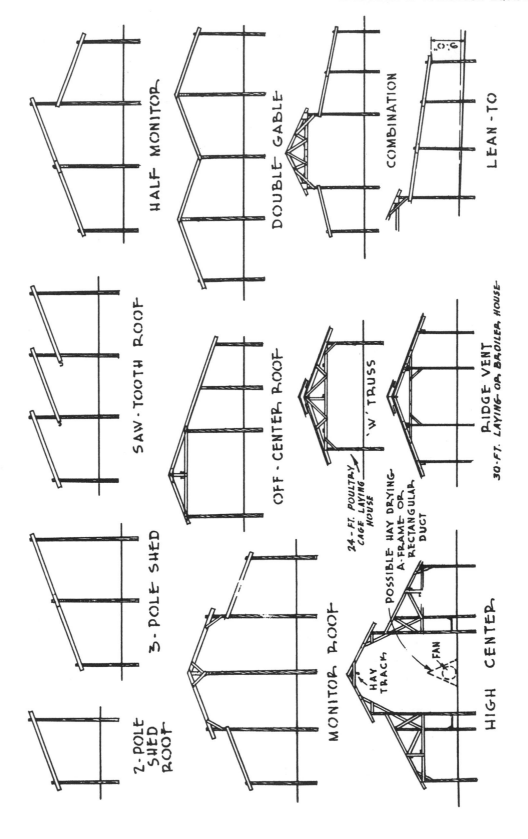

HALF MONITOR

DOUBLE GABLE

COMBINATION

LEAN-TO

SAW-TOOTH ROOF

OFF-CENTER ROOF

'W' TRUSS

24-FT. POULTRY CAGE LAYING HOUSE

RIDGE VENT
30-FT. LAYING OR BROILER HOUSE

3-POLE SHED

2-POLE SHED ROOF

MONITOR ROOF

POSSIBLE HAY DRYING—A-FRAME OR RECTANGULAR DUCT

HAY TRACK

FAN

HIGH CENTER

Cross-section drawings of various pole-type buildings.

Pole-type buildings have a wide variety of uses, yet are economical, very functional, and easily constructed. (Cooperative Extension, Texas A & M University—MP-638)

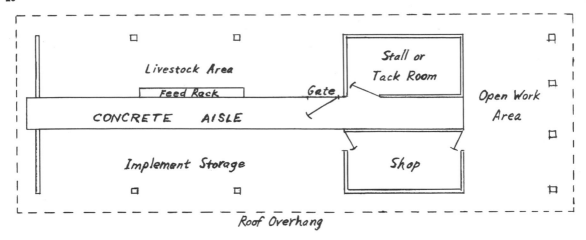

Livestock Area

Feed Rack

CONCRETE   AISLE

Gate

Stall or
Tack Room

Open Work
Area

Implement Storage

Shop

Roof Overhang

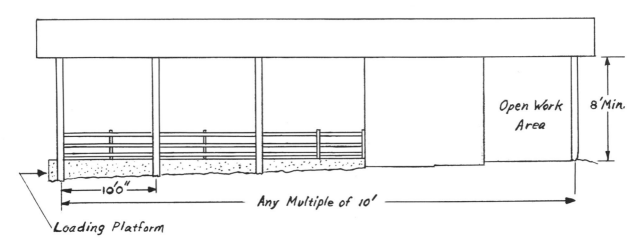

Open Work
Area

8' Min.

10'0"

Any Multiple of 10'

Loading Platform

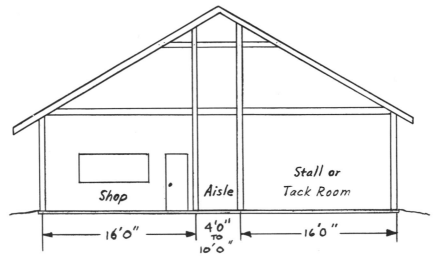

Shop

Aisle

Stall or
Tack Room

16'0"

4'0"
TO
10'0"

16'0"

Section Through Shop

Combination equipment and livestock implement shed.

A ranch headquarters appears neater and more businesslike if there are only a few simple buildings, properly landscaped. Too many small buildings are inefficient, are more expensive to construct, and give a cluttered look. This implement shed has livestock facilities on one side and equipment on the other with a raised concrete walk separating them. The concrete walk also serves as a holding pen, and at one end as a loading chute. There is a shop and open shed area on the other end to work under during hot or wet weather, when saddling horses, brushing animals, or repairing equipment. If additional space is needed use the same basic design and lengthen or widen the entire implement shed to meet space needs.

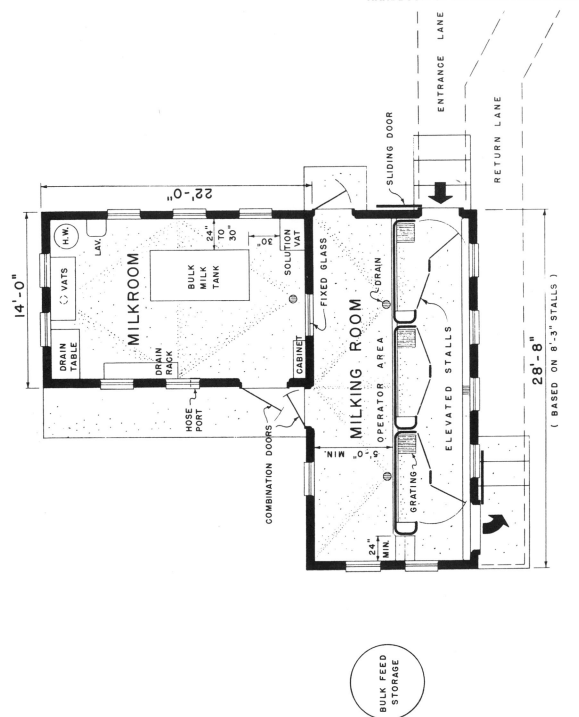

Floor plan of milking plant.

A convenient, practical design for a milking plant. Local codes should be checked before any dairy facilities are decided upon. (Cooperative Extension, Texas A & M University—Plan 5889)

Chapter II

FEEDING AND WATERING EQUIPMENT

Equipment that is well planned and well constructed will improve labor efficiency and save on feed. Sturdy equipment lasts longer and presents a better appearance, so makeshift equipment is out, on the modern ranch. Measurement, angles, bracing, and size of material have important relationships to each other in the construction of feeding and watering equipment. Therefore, the use of properly designed plans will greatly improve the chances of getting desirable equipment as well as save time and labor during its construction. The trend is toward bulk handling of feed, or any other design that will save on labor cost. Self-feeders and ice-free waterers are two examples of equipment that will save labor. In addition, insuring that feed and water are always available results in healthy livestock.

In the long run, concrete or steel equipment welded together will outlast wood. However, wood has many advantages, such as light weight, ease of handling, and low cost of construction. Only quality lumber free from defects—especially knots—should be used, so equipment will be strong and not leak. A major portion of the cost of construction is labor. The use of low-grade lumber wastes high-cost labor.

Directions and measurements or plans should be followed carefully, as spacing and related construction details are important in getting livestock equipment to operate properly.

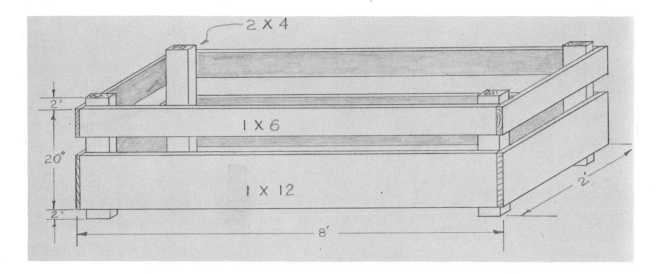

Feed rack for sheep, cattle, or horses.

This rack is light and semiportable; therefore it can easily be moved from field to field. There is no floor, so foreign matter cannot accumulate as the rack can be turned over to clean. Metal braces on the corners will improve its rigidity and make it last longer. One variation is to increase the center spacing to 6 or 8 inches to allow sheep or calves to put their heads into the rack to feed.

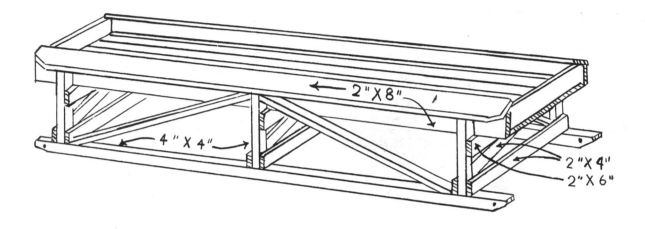

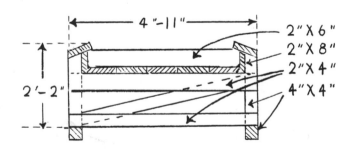

Cattle feed bunk on skids.

A tractor or pickup can tow this feeder easily to a new location.

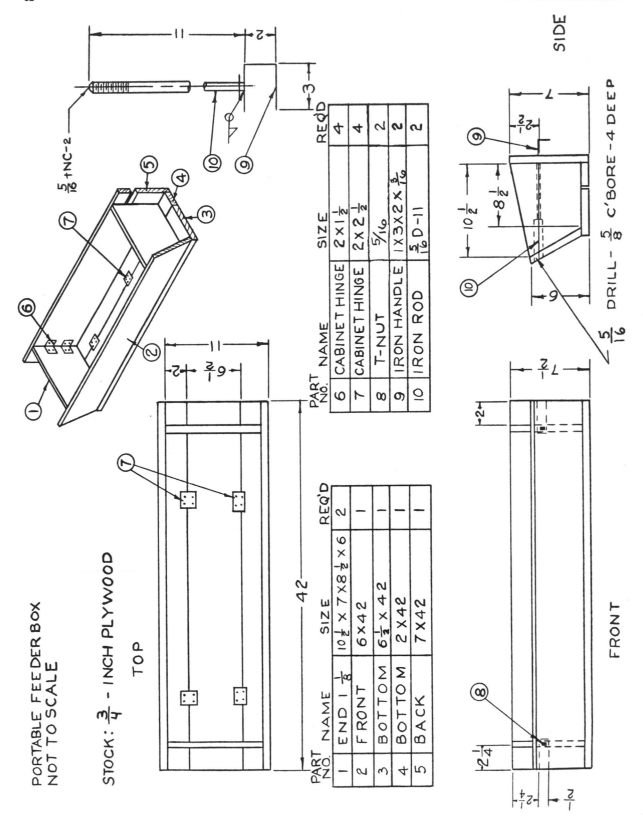

PORTABLE FEEDER BOX
NOT TO SCALE

STOCK: $\frac{3}{4}$ - INCH PLYWOOD

TOP

SIDE

FRONT

$\frac{5}{16}$ + NC-2

DRILL - $\frac{5}{8}$ C'BORE-4 DEEP

$\frac{5}{16}$

PART NO.	NAME	SIZE	REQ'D
6	CABINET HINGE	2×1½	4
7	CABINET HINGE	2×2½	4
8	T-NUT	5/16	2
9	IRON HANDLE	1×3×2×$\frac{3}{16}$	2
10	IRON ROD	$\frac{5}{16}$ D-11	2

PART NO.	NAME	SIZE	REQ'D
1	END	10½×7×8½×6 1-$\frac{1}{8}$	2
2	FRONT	6×42	1
3	BOTTOM	6½×42	1
4	BOTTOM	2×42	1
5	BACK	7×42	1

Collapsible feed box.

This feed box is especially suited for sheep or calves but may also be used for swine. It is particularly useful to exhibitors going to fairs, shows, or exhibitions, as it will fold down compactly to fit into a show box or trunk. Either plywood, ½-inch to ¾-inch, or regular 1-inch surfaced lumber may be used. It should be oiled or painted to preserve it and to keep it from warping so it will be flat and assemble properly. (Robert Paasch, Grass Valley, California)

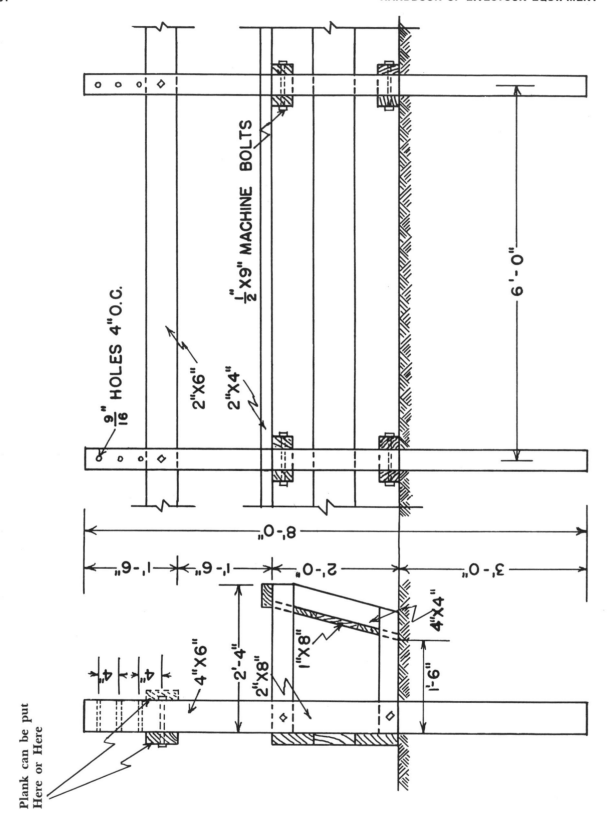

Stationary feed bunk.

This plan does not use a post sunk in the ground at an angle to support the back of the bunk or manger. Holes drilled in the post allow changing the guard rail to the height needed for the size of the animals being fed. (University of Wyoming Circular 148)

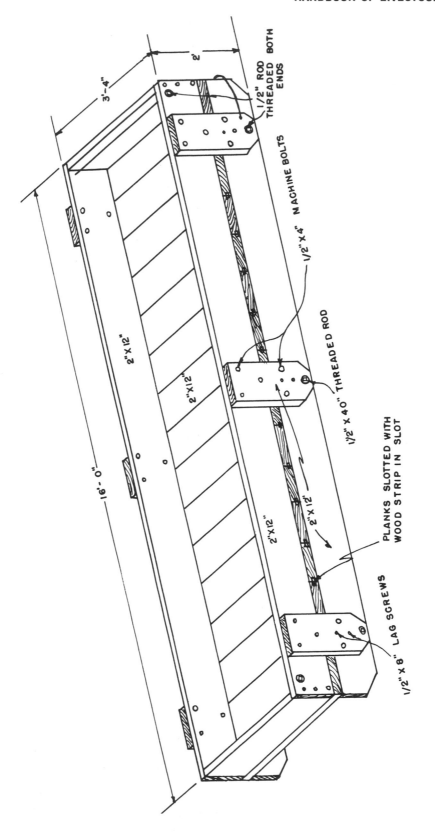

Portable feed bunk.

This type of bunk has been used by feeders and has stood up against very rugged use. The bottom of the bunk is made of treated plank. The planks are slotted, and, as they are laid, a special wood strip is placed in the slot. This prevents cracks from forming between the bottom plank, eliminating grain and feed loss.

The side uprights are fastened to the sides and to the bottom runners with lag screws. A 2" x 6" is set crosswise under the bunk bottom between the uprights. Rods half an inch in diameter and threaded on each end are used as noted in the plan. (University of Wyoming Circular 148)

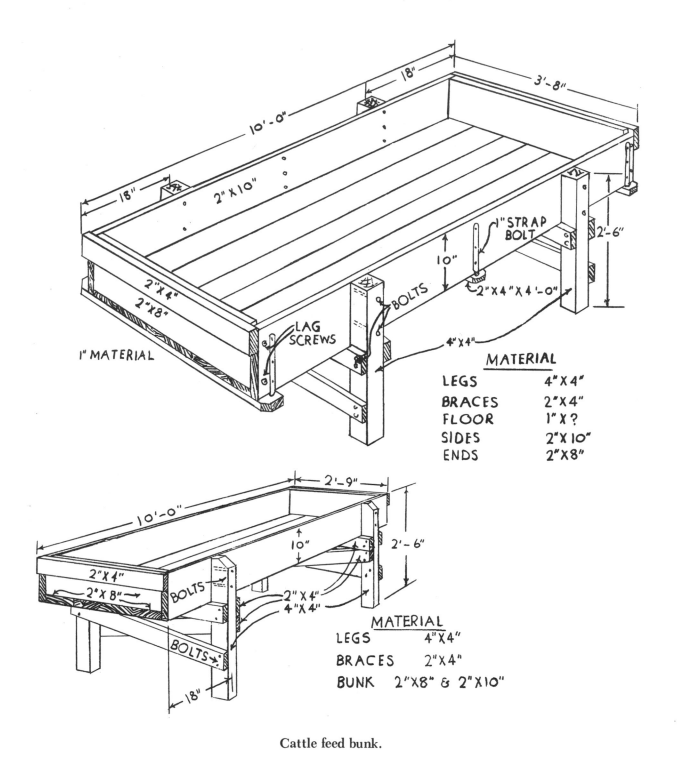

18"

3'-8"

10'-0"

18"

2"X10"

1"STRAP BOLT

2'-6"

10"

2"X4"

2"X8"

2"X4"X4'-0"

LAG SCREWS

BOLTS

4"X4"

1" MATERIAL

MATERIAL

LEGS	4"X4"
BRACES	2"X4"
FLOOR	1"X?
SIDES	2"X10"
ENDS	2"X8"

2'-9"

10'-0"

10"

2'-6"

2"X4"

2"X8"

BOLTS

2"X4"
4"X4"

BOLTS

18"

MATERIAL

LEGS	4"X4"
BRACES	2"X4"
BUNK	2"X8" & 2"X10"

Cattle feed bunk.

This feeder is easy to construct, using everyday materials and a few simple hand tools. It can be used for grain, silage, or pulp.

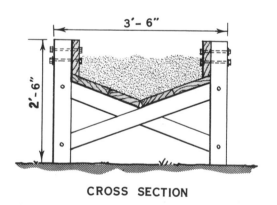

CROSS SECTION

Silage and grain feeding trough.

This trough, 10 feet long and 30 inches wide inside, will feed 10 to 14 head. Construction is simple and sturdy. If permanent installation is desired the posts may be extended into the ground or anchored to concrete pavement. The trough may also be built on skids for easy moving with a tractor. (Plan No. 5766, USDA Agricultural Handbook 81)

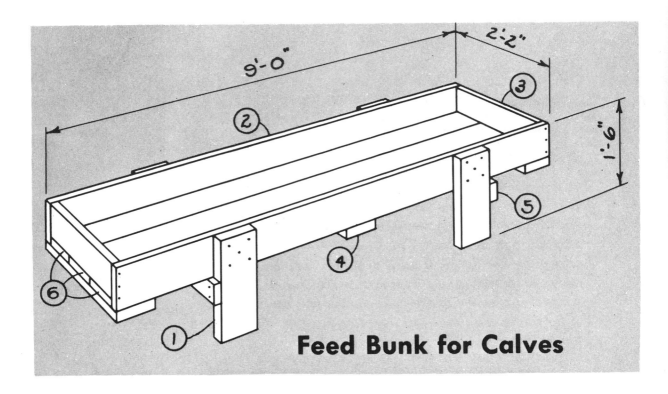

Feed Bunk for Calves

Feed bunk for calves.

A very practical grain bunk for small calves. It is only 18 inches high and three 2 x 8's wide. Then, too, it can be used for yearlings or any of the show cattle. Many breeders use this same type bunk in the show barn. If it is to be placed against a wall, the legs on one side should be extended 20 inches so that a back of 1-inch lumber can be added; it will save feed.

BILL OF MATERIALS

Item	Quantity	Description
1	4	2x8—1 ft. 6 in.
2	2	2x8—9 ft. 0 in.
3	2	2x6—1 ft. 10½ in.
4	3	2x8—2 ft. 2 in.
5	2	2x6—2 ft. 6 in.
6	3	2x8—9 ft. 0 in.

Hardware

Use 20d common wire nails to make all joints. Clinch where possible.

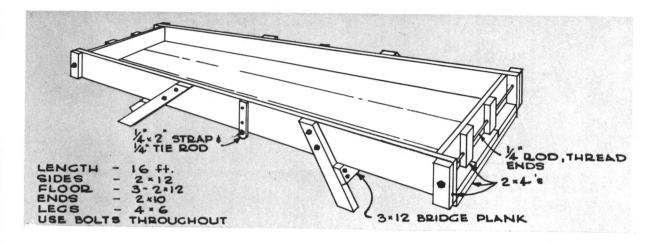

LENGTH - 16 ft.
SIDES - 2×12
FLOOR - 3-2×12
ENDS - 2×10
LEGS - 4×6
USE BOLTS THROUGHOUT

¼"×2" STRAP &
¼" TIE ROD

¼" ROD, THREAD ENDS

2×4's

3×12 BRIDGE PLANK

Feed or silage bunk for mature cattle.

This feeder is sturdy, and difficult for livestock to move or push.

BILL OF MATERIALS

Quantity	Description
5	2x12—16 ft. sides and floor
2	2x10— 2 ft. 10 in. ends
2	3x12— 3 ft. 10 in. cross ties
2	2x 6— 3 ft. 1¼ in. cross ties
2	2x 4— 1 ft. 1⅛ in. end cleats
4	2x 4— 0 ft. 11½ in. end cleats
2	2 in. x ¼ in. strap iron, 13 in. long
2	⅜ in. rods, 40¼ in. long
1	⅜ in. rod, 37⅝ in. long

(American Hereford Association)

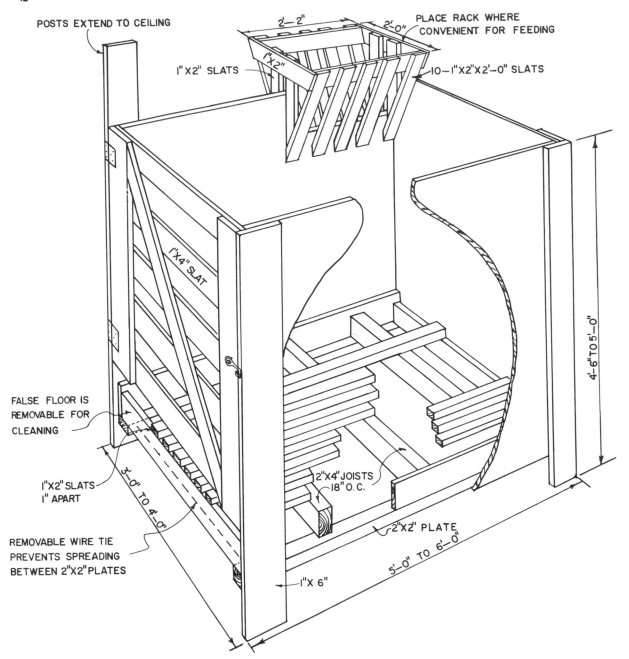

POSTS EXTEND TO CEILING

PLACE RACK WHERE CONVENIENT FOR FEEDING

2—2"

2'-0"

1"X2" SLATS

1"X2"

10—1"X2"X2'-0" SLATS

1"X4" SLAT

4'-6"TO 5'-0"

FALSE FLOOR IS REMOVABLE FOR CLEANING

1"X2" SLATS 1" APART

3'-0" TO 4'-0"

REMOVABLE WIRE TIE PREVENTS SPREADING BETWEEN 2"X2" PLATES

2"X4" JOISTS 18" O.C.

2"X2" PLATE

5'-0" TO 6'-0"

1"X 6"

Individual calf pen and feeder.

Calf pens should be equipped with a hay rack, grain box, and water bowl. A calf building should have a fan to control temperature as well as ventilation. This individual calf pen has slats that can be removed for easy cleaning. The hay rack can be placed on either side, as it provides feeding space for two calves. If desired, the partitions between the pens can be constructed so they are removable for convenient cleaning. (Fact Sheet 148, University of Maryland)

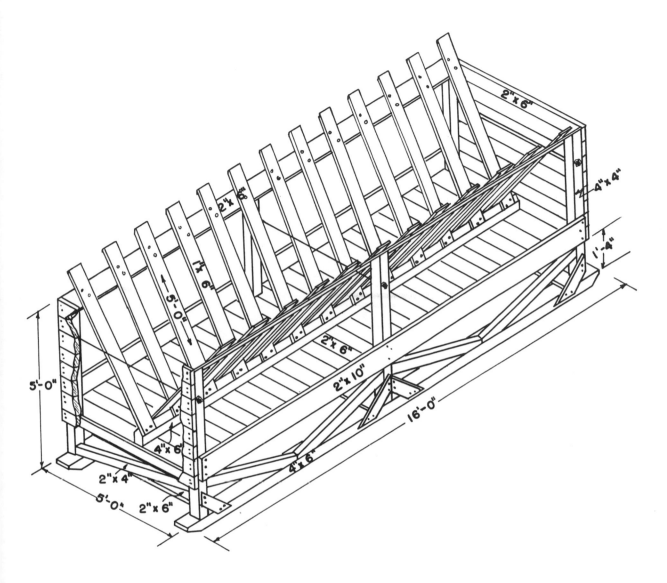

Portable feed rack.

There are many different types of hay feeders; one type often seen is shown here. This portable rack for feeding hay can be used in the corral or pasture. When filled, it will hold 160 cubic feet— even more, if it is rounded off at the top. This rack is rugged in construction. It catches the leaves and fine stems that drop off as the hay is pulled out between the slats. That means a saving of the best part of the hay.

However, this type feeder is sometimes criticized as wasting too much hay. But correct spacing of the slats will solve the wastage problem. For flaked baled hay and long hay, slats should be from 3½ to 5½ inches apart. If round bales are to be fed, the spacing should be about 7½ inches. (University of Wyoming Circular 148)

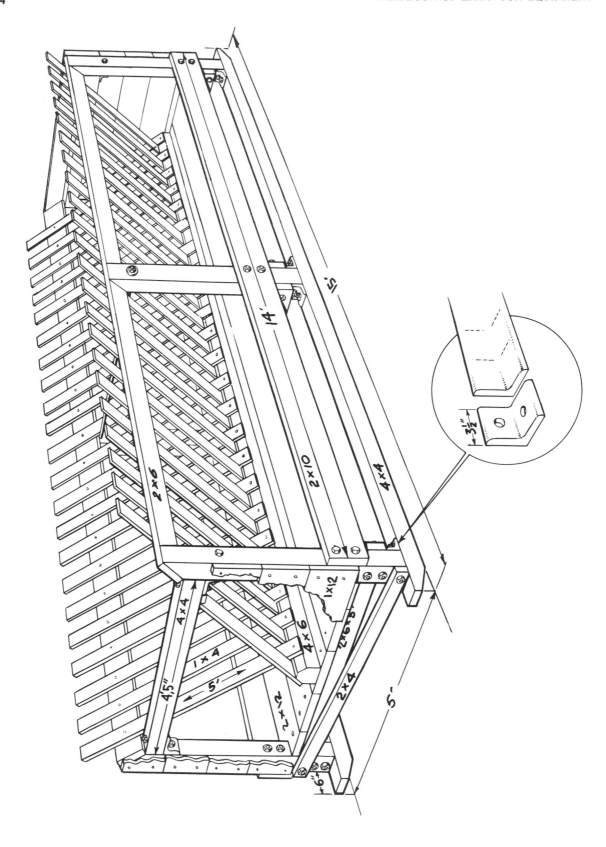

2×6

14'

5'

2×10

4×4

3½"

4×4

1×4

4×6

1×12

2×6×5

4.5"

5'

2×2

2×4

5'

6"

Hay feeder.

This type of hay feeder is seen everywhere. For flaked baled hay, the spacing between the slats should be 3½ to 5½ inches, whereas if round bales are to be fed the spacing will need be approximately 7½ inches. This type feeder is often criticized as wasting too much hay. The correct spacing of the slats seems to be the key to the wastage problem.

BILL OF MATERIALS

Quantity	Description
2	4x 4—16 ft. runners
6	4x 4— 5 ft. posts
2	4x 4— 4 ft. 5 in. cross ties
4	2x 6— 5 ft. cross ties
2	2x10—14 ft. sides
5	2x12—14 ft. floor
1	4x 6—14 ft. center rail
46	1x 4— 5 ft. slats
8	1x12— 5 ft. ends
2	2x 4— 5 ft. end braces
12	3½ in. angle iron corner braces
16	5 in. x ½ in. mch. head bolts
26	7 in. x ½ in. mch. head bolts
4	9 in. x ½ in. mch. head bolts
1	5 ft. 1 in. x ½ in. rod cross ties

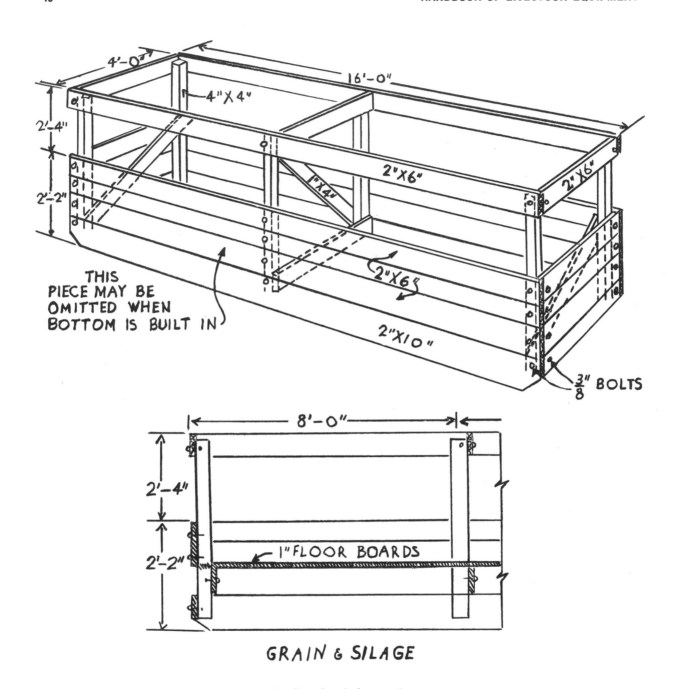

Feeding bunk for cattle.

Construction of a grain and silage-feeding bunk is the same as a hay bunk with a floor added. (Montana State University)

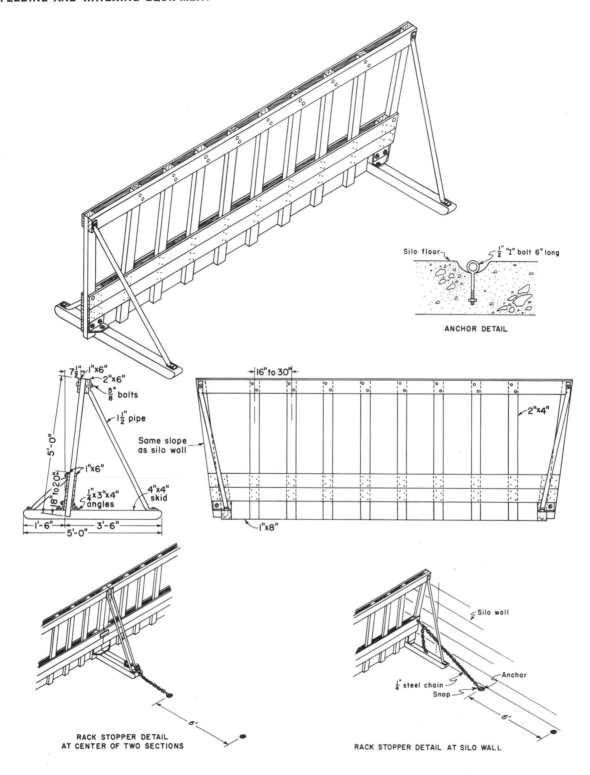

Movable self-feeder rack.

(USDA Plan Ex. 5801)

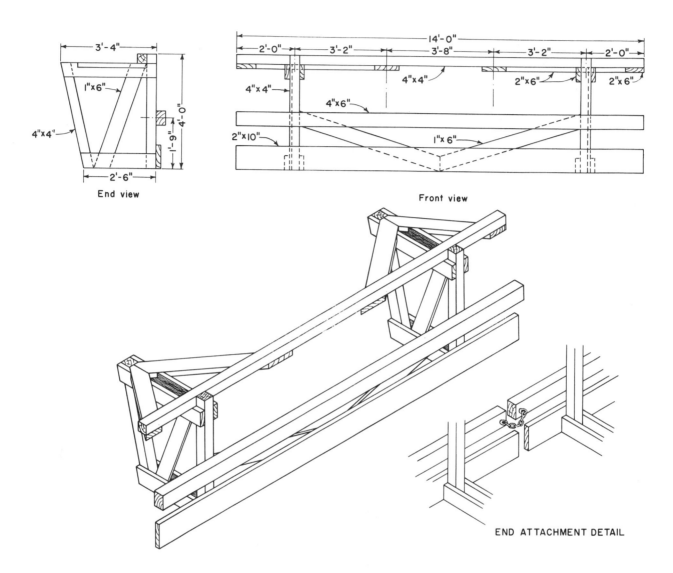

Wooden bumper-type self-feeder.

Consider these points when building and using the wooden bumper-type self-feeder.

1. The 4" x 4" uprights rest against the silage and limit the amount of silage the animals can obtain. Before the animals can push the feeder forward, the silage must be removed from behind the uprights with a fork. This is usually done once each day.

2. It may be necessary to vary the depth of the feeder from its front face to the 4" x 4" uprights for various sizes of cows. The dimensions shown are generally satisfactory in permitting average-sized cows to reach the silage.

3. If a silo wider than 14 feet is used, build two sections and tie them together at the center as shown in the lower right-hand corner.

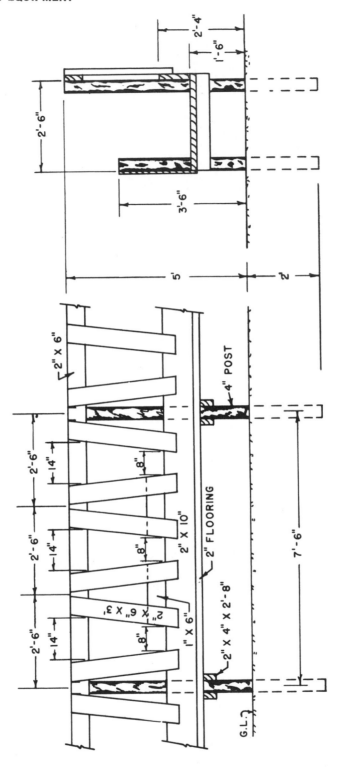

Cattle-feeding rack.

Scale ½'' = 1'0''. (Agricultural Engineering Dept., Virginia Polytechnic Institute)

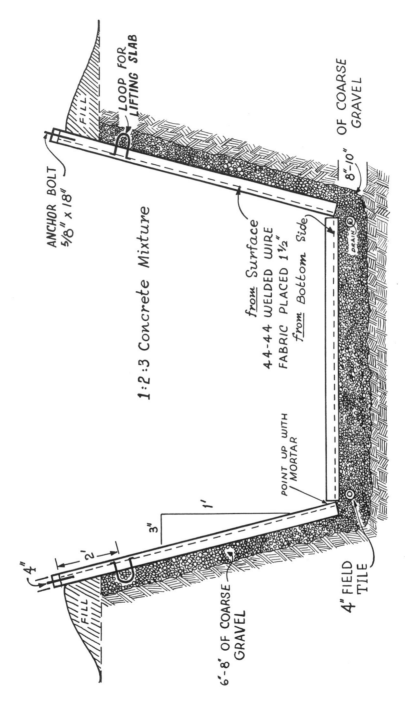

Cross-section sketch of typical trench silo.

(Connecticut Agricultural Extension Bulletin 149)

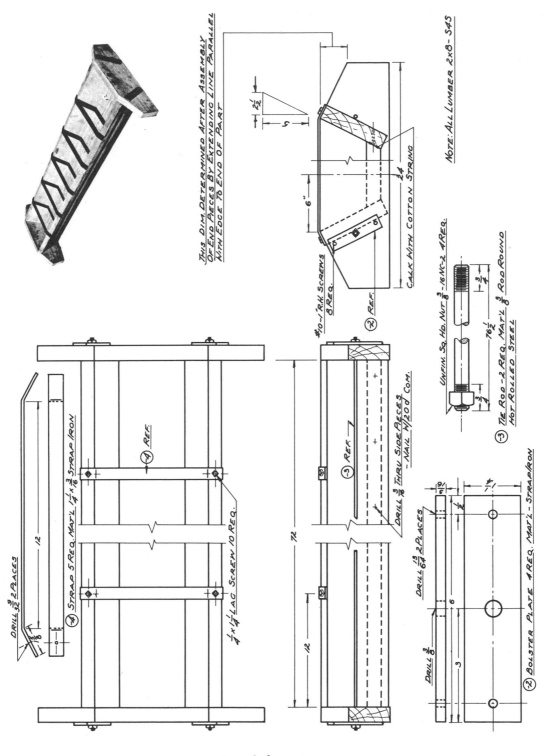

Trough for swine.

This feeder is tight enough to hold most liquids and sturdy enough to hold up when reinforced as illustrated.

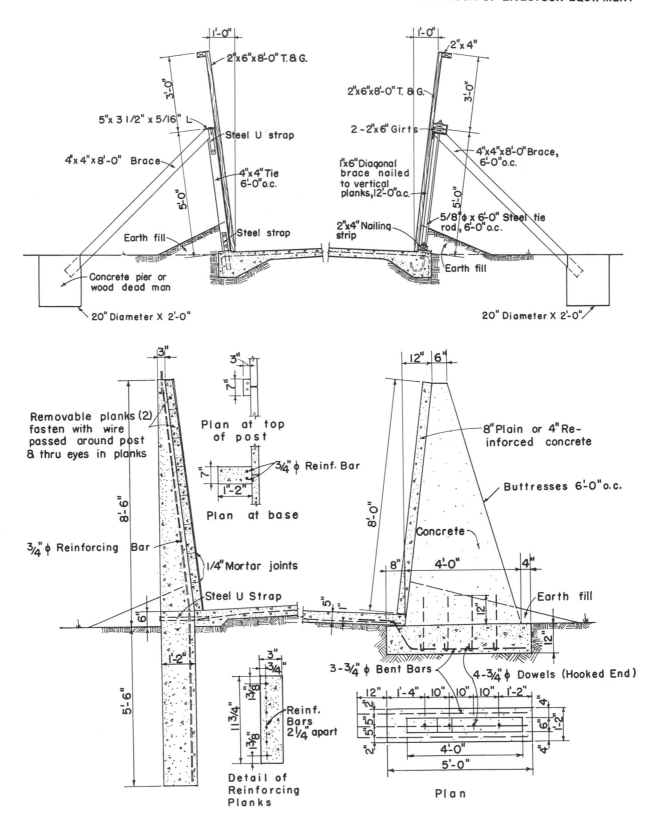

1'-0"
2"x6"x8'-0" T. & G.
3'-0"
5"x 3 1/2" x 5/16" L
Steel U strap
4"x4"x8'-0" Brace
4"x4" Tie 6'-0" o.c.
5'-0"
Earth fill
Steel strap
Concrete pier or wood dead man
20" Diameter X 2'-0"

1'-0"
2" x 4"
2"x6"x8'-0" T. & G.
3'-0"
2 - 2"x6" Girts
4"x4"x8'-0" Brace, 6'-0" o.c.
1"x6" Diagonal brace nailed to vertical planks, 12'-0" o.c.
5'-0"
5/8"Φ x 6'-0" Steel tie rod, 6'-0" o.c.
2"x4" Nailing strip
Earth fill
20" Diameter X 2'-0"

3"
Removable planks (2) fasten with wire passed around post & thru eyes in planks
8'-6"
3/4" Φ Reinforcing Bar
1/4" Mortar joints
Steel U Strap
6"
1'-2"
5'-6"

3"
7"
Plan at top of post
3/4" Φ Reinf. Bar
7"
1'-2"
Plan at base

3"
3/4"
3/8"
11 3/4"
3/8"
Reinf. Bars 2 1/4 apart
Detail of Reinforcing Planks

12" 6"
8'-0"
8"Plain or 4"Re-inforced concrete
Buttresses 6'-0" o.c.
Concrete
8" 4'-0" 4"
Earth fill
5" 1"
12"
12"
3-3/4" Φ Bent Bars
4-3/4" Φ Dowels (Hooked End)

12" 1'-4" 10" 10" 10" 1'-2"
4"
2 1/2"
6"
1'-2"
2"
4"
4'-0"
5'-0"
Plan

Types of walls for bunker silos.

The walls of bunker silos can be made from a variety of materials, but they must be strong and able to withstand the pressure of heavy silage. Wood, steel, concrete, or block is used, but must be securely braced. In the cross section several materials are illustrated, including steel or wooden beams reaching out to a sunken concrete pier. Posts of steel, wood, or concrete are suitable if they are deep enough (generally 5 to 6 feet) in the ground. One popular and functional method is to use a concrete buttress to support the silo walls. (USDA Bulletin 149)

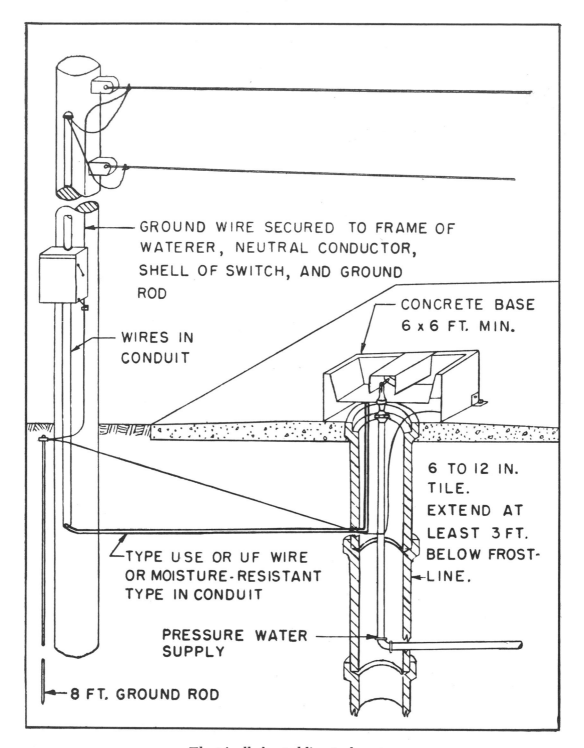

GROUND WIRE SECURED TO FRAME OF
WATERER, NEUTRAL CONDUCTOR,
SHELL OF SWITCH, AND GROUND
ROD

WIRES IN
CONDUIT

CONCRETE BASE
6 x 6 FT. MIN.

6 TO 12 IN.
TILE.
EXTEND AT
LEAST 3 FT.
BELOW FROST-
LINE.

TYPE USE OR UF WIRE
OR MOISTURE-RESISTANT
TYPE IN CONDUIT

PRESSURE WATER
SUPPLY

8 FT. GROUND ROD

Electrically heated livestock waterer.

This waterer is easily installed if details are followed. (USDA Leaflet 395)

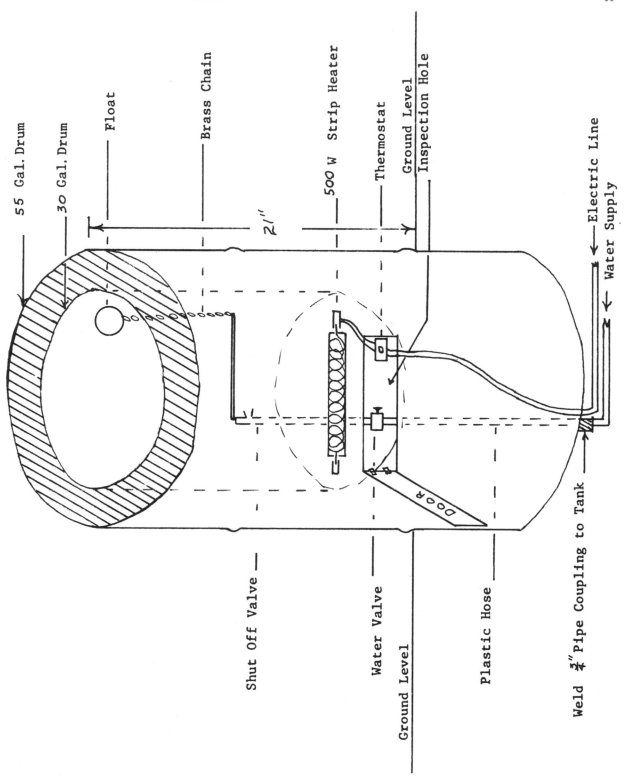

Automatically heated stock-watering system.

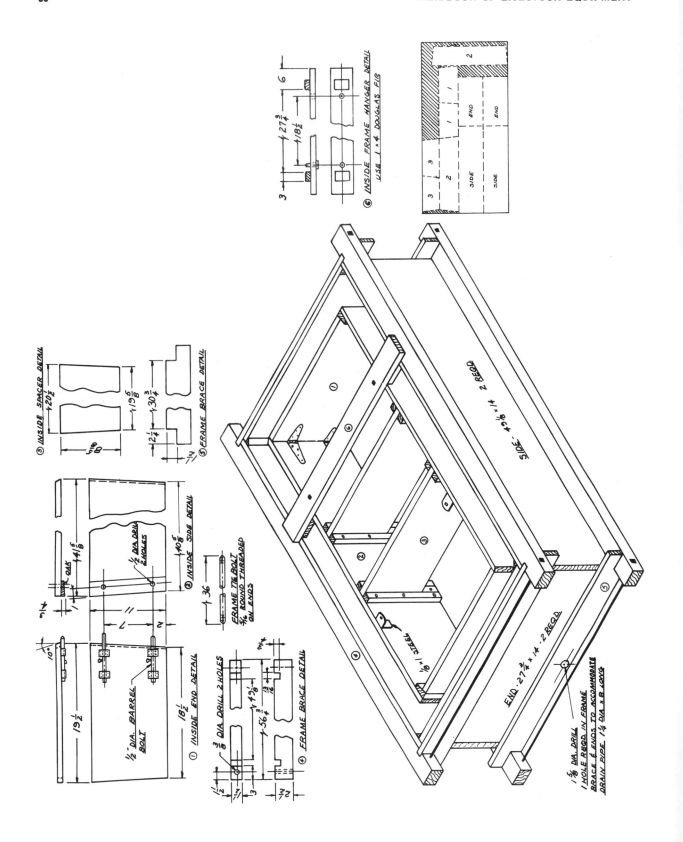

Water trough (concrete).

The forms illustrated enable anyone handy with tools to be able to pour his own concrete watering trough. These forms collapse readily, so they can be used over and over. (Agricultural Engineering Dept., California State Polytechnic College, San Luis Obispo)

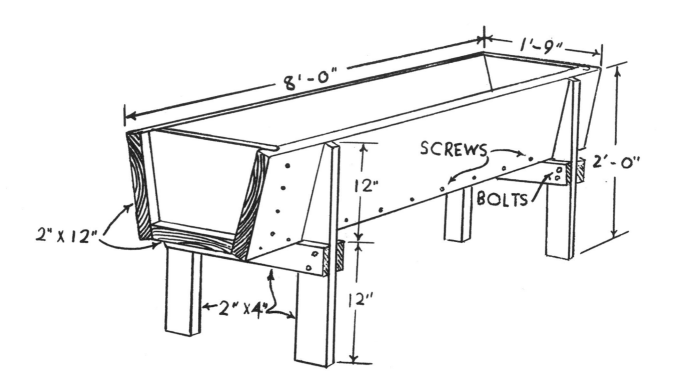

Watering trough for cattle.

Rabbet sides and bottom for end piece. White lead all joints. (Montana State University)

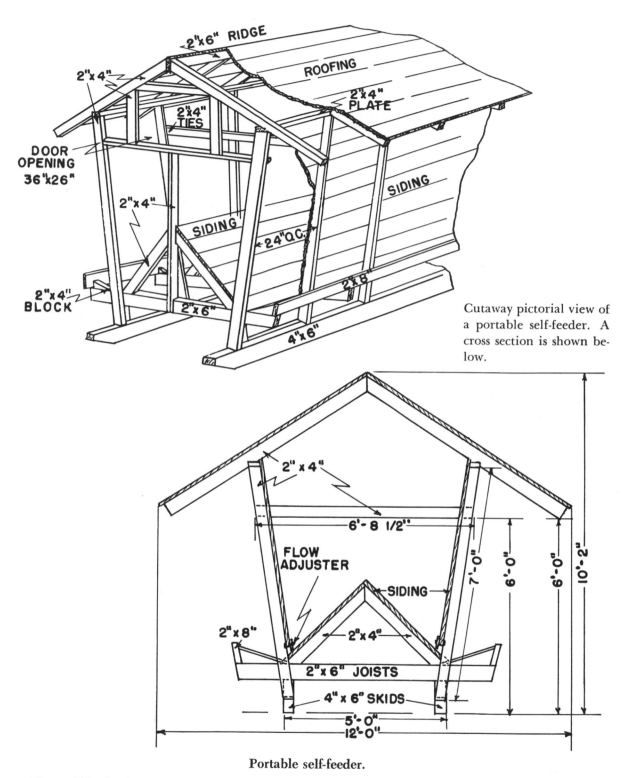

2"x6" RIDGE

ROOFING

2"x4"

2"x4" PLATE

2"x4" TIES

DOOR OPENING 36"x26"

SIDING

2"x4"

SIDING

24"O.C.

2"x8"

2"x4" BLOCK

2"x6"

4"x6"

Cutaway pictorial view of a portable self-feeder. A cross section is shown below.

2" x 4"

6'- 8 1/2"

FLOW ADJUSTER

SIDING

7'-0"

6'-0"

6'-0"

10'-2"

2"x 8"

2" x 4"

2"x 6" JOISTS

4" x 6" SKIDS

5'-0"

12'-0"

Portable self-feeder.

The self-feeder has a door at each end to facilitate filling. It is 12 feet long and holds about 150 bushels of grain. (Colorado A. & M. University Bulletin 441-A)

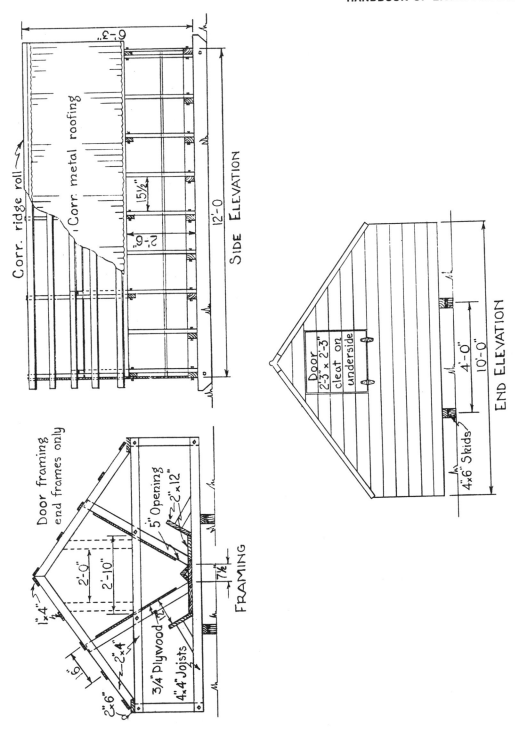

Creep feeder.

This self-feeding creep feeder for calves is mounted on skids. It is a complete unit, yet is readily portable. The bin holds about 1,000 pounds of feed concentrates. (University of California Circular 414)

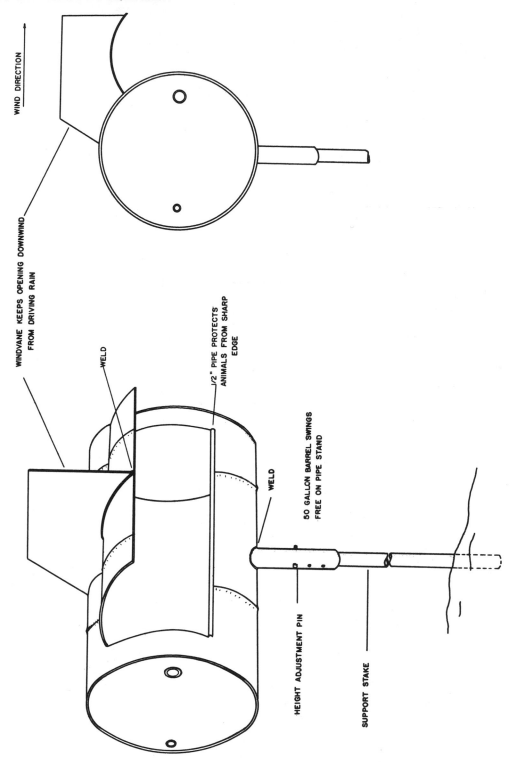

WIND DIRECTION

WINDVANE KEEPS OPENING DOWNWIND FROM DRIVING RAIN

WELD

1/2" PIPE PROTECTS ANIMALS FROM SHARP EDGE

WELD

50 GALLON BARREL SWINGS FREE ON PIPE STAND

HEIGHT ADJUSTMENT PIN

SUPPORT STAKE

Stock mineral feeder.

(Division of Agricultural Engineering, University of California, Davis)

Cutaway pictorial view
of a portable self-feeder
for a calf creep.

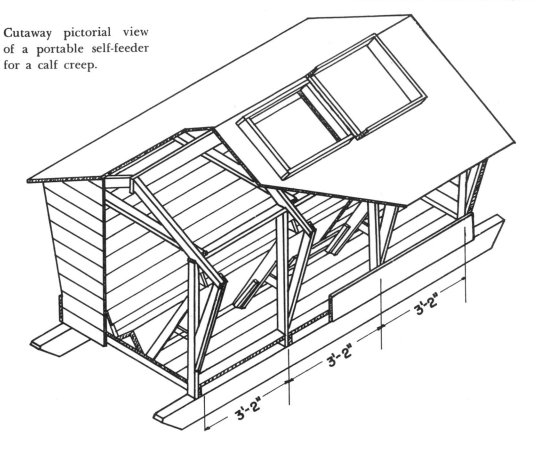

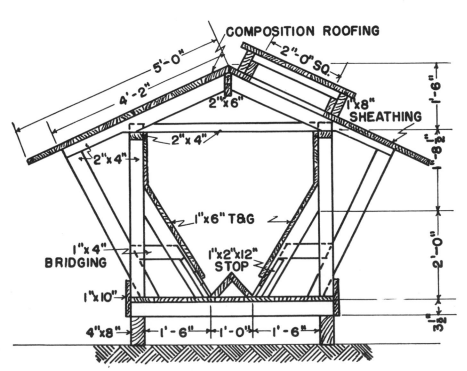

Cross section of the self-feeder shown above. The stop is made adjustable to vary the depth of the opening, thus allowing different feeds. Allow 6 to 8 inches of space per calf having access to self-feeder.

Portable self-feeder.

A good many breeders are getting back to the original creep-feeding plan of having a self-feeder in a pen which only the calves can enter. Thus, this type of feeder and suggested pen is shown. It is felt calves will learn to eat grain more quickly under this arrangement. Then, too, a small hay feeder can be provided if desired, and a separate salt box supplied for the calves.

Modern portable-type calf creeps require no fence. These are built strong, and this feature is essential. Feeders of this type built skimpy will be torn up by cows or heifers which were creep-fed as calves.

BILL OF MATERIALS

Item	Quantity	Description
1	2	4x 8—12 ft. 0 in. runners
2	2	1x10— 9 ft. 9 in. side of feed hopper
3	100 sq. ft.	1x 8 sheathing, roof
4	8	2x 4— 4 ft. 2 in. rafters
5	4	2x 4— 4 ft. 7¼ in. cross plate
6	2	2x 4— 9 ft. 7½ in. top plate
7	8	2x 4— 4 ft. 0 in. vert. studs
8	4	2x 4— 4 ft. 7¼ in. base cross plate
9	80 sq. ft.	1x 6 tongued and grooved floor
10	1	2x10— 9 ft. 7½ in. bin "V"
11	1	2x 8— 9 ft. 7¼ in. bin "V"
12	8	2x 4— 3 ft. 0 in. feed box studs
13	8	2x 4— 4 ft. 0 in. rafter brace
14	4	2x 4— 3 ft. 0 in. filler
15	54 sq. ft.	1x 6 tongued and grooved feed box ends
16	12	1x 2 slide stops
17	6	1x 6— 3 ft. 2 in. feed control
18	8 lin. ft.	2x 6 door
19	3 lin. ft.	2x 2 door
20	10 lin. ft.	2x 4 door
21	5 sq. ft.	1x 6 sheathing, door
	1	piano hinge—2 ft. 0 in.
	100 sq. ft.	roofing

(Colorado A & M University Bulletin 441-A)

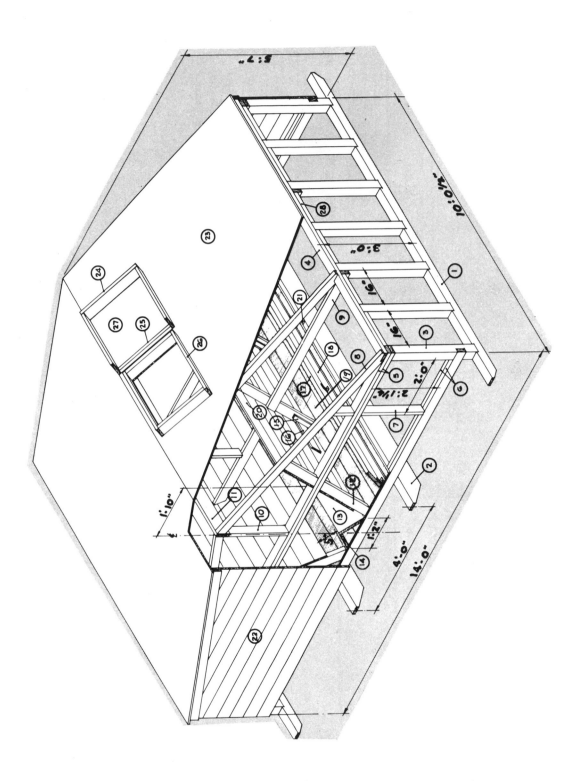

Creep feeder with built-in fence.

A feeder designed to eliminate the cross braces which the calves cross over unless they back out. The 4'' x 4'' space blocks are strong enough to last.

Combining the calf creep with a sun shade for the calves has proved worthwhile. An advantage is that a less expensive feeder can be used, as the sun shade roof protects the grain.

BILL OF MATERIALS

Item	Quantity	Description
1	2	4x 4—12 ft. 0 in. runner
2	2	4x 8—12 ft. 0 in. runner
3	14	4x 4— 3 ft. ¾ in. vert. studs
4	2	2x 4—10 ft. ½ in. top plate
5	4	2x 4—14 ft. 0 in. top plate
6	4	2x 4—14 ft. 0 in. cross plate
7	4	2x 4— 3 ft. 0 in. vert. stud
8	8	2x 4— 8 ft. 0 in. rafters
9	4	2x 4—14 ft. 0 in. cross bridging
10	4	2x 4— 2 ft. 4 in. vert.
11	1	2x 6—10 ft. ½ in. ridge plate
12	8	2x 4— 5 ft. 0 in. knee bracing
13	1	2x10—10 ft. ½ in. bin V
14	1	2x 8—10 ft. ½ in. bin V
15	12	1x 2—12 in. feed box slide stops
16	6	1x 6— 3 ft. 4 in. feed box slide
17	2	2x 8—10 ft. 0 in. feed box slide
18	2	1x 3—10 ft. ½ in. feed box slide
19	10	1x 6—10 ft. ½ in. feed box fl.
20	110 sq. ft.	car siding—feed box slides
21	2	2x 4— 5 ft. 0 in. feed box fl. supp.
22	140 sq. ft.	car siding—ends
23	150 sq. ft.	car siding—roof
24	1	2x 6— 4 ft. 7 in. feed door
25	1	2x 2— 2 ft. 4 in. feed door
26	1	2x 4— 8 ft. 8 in. feed door
27	6 sq. ft.	1x 6— feed door
28	12	2x 4— 1 ft. 4 in.
	8	strap hinges, 6 in. long
	1	piano hinge, 2 ft. 0 in. long
	150 sq. ft.	roofing

(American Hereford Association)

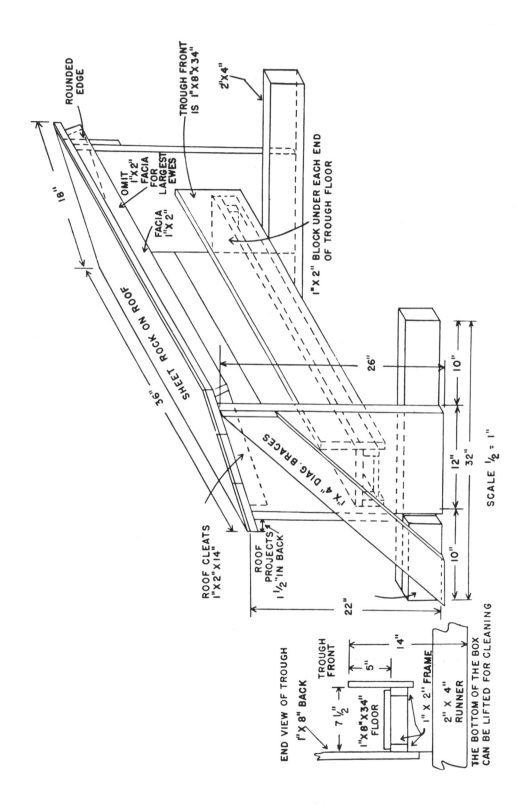

ROUNDED EDGE

TROUGH FRONT IS 1"X8"X34"

2"X4"

18"

OMIT 1"x2" FACIA FOR LARGEST EWES

FACIA 1"X 2"

1"X 2" BLOCK UNDER EACH END OF TROUGH FLOOR

36"

SHEET ROCK ON ROOF

26"

10"

12"

32"

ROOF CLEATS 1"X2"X14"

ROOF PROJECTS 1½"IN BACK

1"X 4" DIAG. BRACES

10"

22"

SCALE ½ = 1"

END VIEW OF TROUGH

1"X 8" BACK

TROUGH FRONT

14"

5"

7½"

1"X8"X34" FLOOR

1" X 2" FRAME

2"X 4" RUNNER

THE BOTTOM OF THE BOX CAN BE LIFTED FOR CLEANING

Mineral box.

Note: To increase the capacity of this feeder, increase its length. The side or view dimensions should not be altered.

BILL OF MATERIALS

2 pcs. 2''x 4''x32'' runners
2 pcs. 1''x12''x26'' sides
2 pcs. 1''x 8''x36'' back
3 pcs. 1''x 6''x36'' roof
2 pcs. 1''x 4''x 9'' space blocks
2 pcs. 1''x 2''x14'' roof cleats
1 pc. 1''x 2''x36'' facia board
2 pcs. 1''x 8''x34'' trough front floor
2 pcs. 1''x 2''x34'' trough front base
2 pcs. 1''x 2''x 5'' trough floor base

(Clemson University, Agricultural College Circular 404)

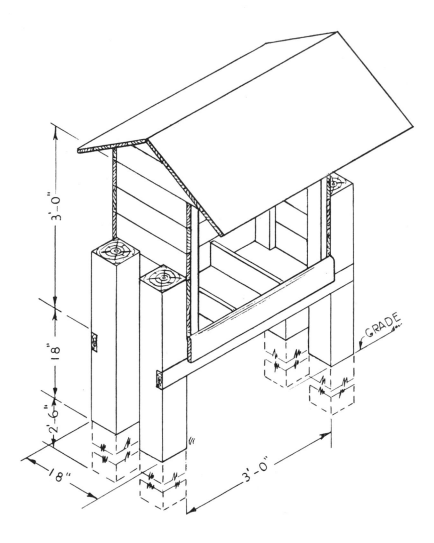

Salt box.

Cattle should have salt available at all times. Mature beef cows will consume from 1 to 2.5 pounds of salt per month on range and pasture. It is practically impossible for cattle to get enough salt from a block to meet their needs and desires.

Ground salt is a must if the cattleman expects to take proper care of the salt requirements of his cattle. This salt should be iodized. Salt will need to be protected from the weather—especially rain or snow—or it will cake. Heavy metal boxes may be necessary where porcupines chew up wooden boxes.

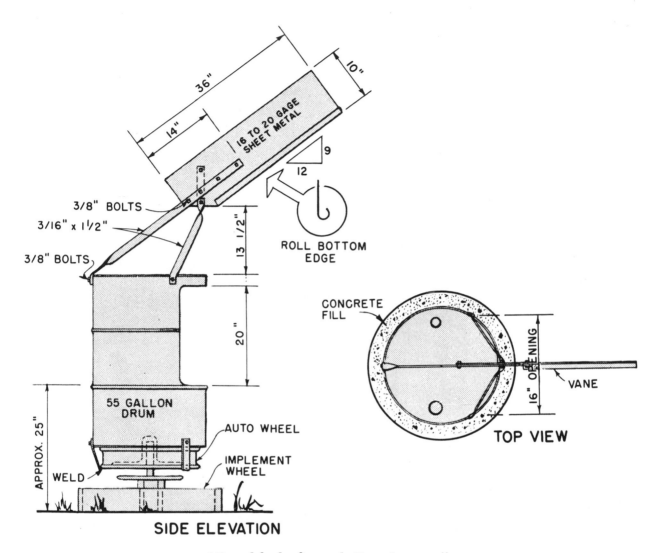

36"

14"

10"

16 TO 20 GAGE
SHEET METAL

9

12

3/8" BOLTS

3/16" x 1 1/2"

3/8" BOLTS

13 1/2"

ROLL BOTTOM
EDGE

CONCRETE
FILL

20"

16" OPENING

VANE

55 GALLON
DRUM

AUTO WHEEL

IMPLEMENT
WHEEL

TOP VIEW

APPROX. 25"

WELD

SIDE ELEVATION

Mineral feeder for cattle "weathervane."

This mineral feeder swivels so that the opening faces away from the wind. It is assembled from a 55-gallon drum, an old automobile front wheel and axle assembly, and other odds and ends around the farm.

Burrs and sharp edges should be removed from the opening in the drum. The inside of the drum should be coated with asphalt paint. Other metal parts should be protected with a preservative paint that does not contain lead.

For proper operation, the feeder should be set on a level surface. (USDA Miscellaneous Publication 775)

Chapter III

FENCES AND GATES

The success of a livestock operation is dependent upon satisfactory control of animals through the use of fences and gates. Furthermore, the beauty and efficiency of operation relate to the type of construction, location of fences and gates, and kind of material and workmanship utilized. The most obvious indicator of the type of rancher or condition of the business is the appearance of fences and gates and in most cases it is the first thing a visitor notices. A properly constructed fence, typical of the locality and well kept up, is the classic symbol of the good life in the open. Good fences can regulate grazing in pastures so as to make for better management. They may save the operator from financial loss, should livestock break out on a highway; not only from death loss, but the prevention of a costly lawsuit.

There is a fence and gate for each purpose. Horses, for example, need board fences, especially if they are confined in small areas. This is also true with all types of livestock if they are to be crowded in any way. Fences are necessary, but upkeep is continuous, so they should be well built. Labor cost is high, and well built fences will save tremendously in repair and upkeep.

Lumber or pipe fences are the most expensive, so wire fences tend to be used more than other types.

In smaller grass paddocks which may be used for calves alone, it is usually more satisfactory if woven wire is used, if boards, pipe, or poles are not practical. For these either 32- or 39-inch woven wire is most often used with three barbed wires placed above, making the total height 47 to 54 inches. On farms where hogs are produced, a barbed wire placed 1 inch below the woven wire is essential.

For a number of years barbed wire manufacturers made what was known as cattle and hog wire, depending on the spacing of the barbs. Today all barbed wire sold has the barbs spaced the same.

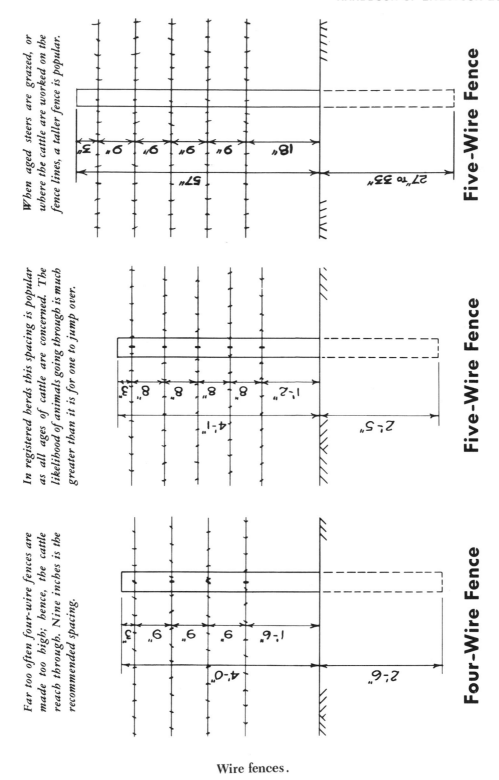

When aged steers are grazed, or where the cattle are worked on the fence lines, a taller fence is popular.

Five-Wire Fence

In registered herds this spacing is popular as all ages of cattle are concerned. The likelihood of animals going through is much greater than it is for one to jump over.

Five-Wire Fence

Far too often four-wire fences are made too high; hence, the cattle reach through. Nine inches is the recommended spacing.

Four-Wire Fence

Wire fences.

The overall height of a barbed wire fence is less important than the spacing of wires in such a way that cattle will seldom get their heads through.

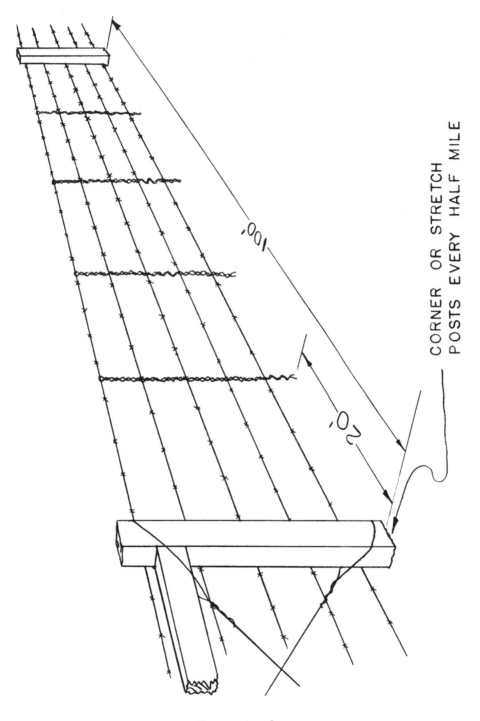

Suspension fence.

This fence is fast and economical to construct, and a very satisfactory range fence. It is constructed with line posts 100 feet apart, with well-braced corner or stretch posts at ½ mile intervals, and spiral wire stays at 20-foot intervals.

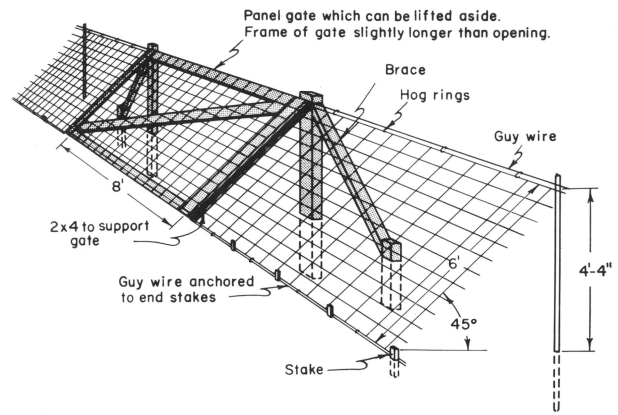

Panel gate which can be lifted aside.
Frame of gate slightly longer than opening.

Brace

Hog rings

Guy wire

8'

2 x 4 to support
gate

Guy wire anchored
to end stakes

6'

4'-4"

45°

Stake

Typical slanting deer fencing with panel gate. Gate support may be sunk into ground to provide
sufficient anchor for the bottom guy wire.

Deer fence.

This slanting fence is effective because it acts as a psychological barrier to deer. Deer usually try to crawl under, but become discouraged and seldom jump because of the slanting nature of the fence. It is used where a higher fence would be unsightly. The biggest disadvantage is that domestic livestock damage it too easily. (University of California Circular 514)

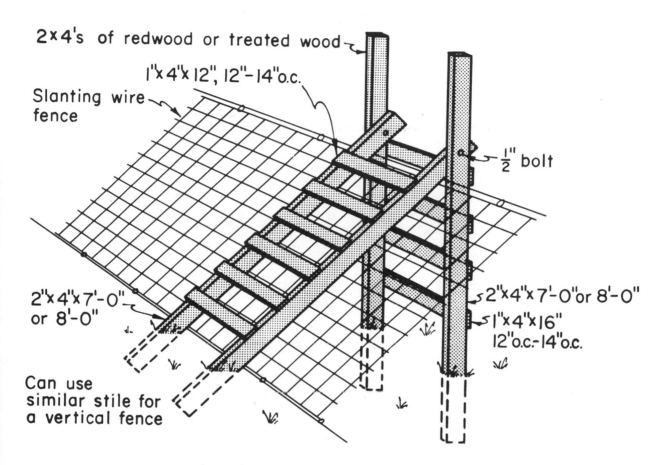

2×4's of redwood or treated wood

1"x 4"x 12", 12"–14"o.c.

Slanting wire fence

½" bolt

2"x4"x7'-0" or 8'-0"

2"x4"x 7'-0"or 8'-0"

1"x4"x16" 12"o.c.-14"o.c.

Can use similar stile for a vertical fence

A simple stile for foot access over a slanting fence.

It can also be constructed over a vertical fence. (University of California Circular 514)

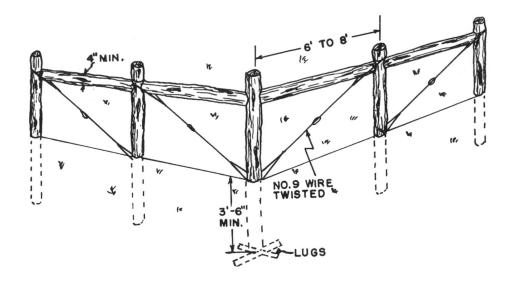

4" MIN.

6' TO 8'

NO.9 WIRE
TWISTED

3'-6" MIN.

LUGS

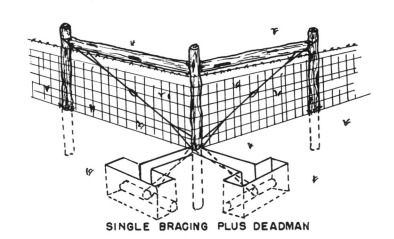

SINGLE BRACING PLUS DEADMAN

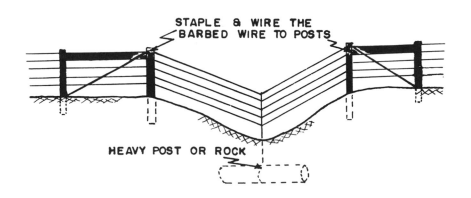

STAPLE & WIRE THE
BARBED WIRE TO POSTS

HEAVY POST OR ROCK

Bracing corner fence posts.

According to University of Wyoming Circular 148, fence corner construction is the critical factor in the successful performance of a wire fence. Horizontally braced end spans with a diagonal brace wire and end post lugs, are best. A single span may be used for a fence length of 10 rods or less, double span for 10 to 40 rods and a 3-span assembly for fences over 40 rods in length.

For single spans, lugs or deadmen must be used for best results. Deadmen require considerable work; lugs do the job with less labor. The double span is recommended in place of the single span to avoid the extra work, and it gives longer life to the fence.

Increasing the depth of set of the post from 2½ feet to 3½ feet almost doubles the holding power.

The minimum-size horizontal brace to use in spans up to 8 feet is 4 inches. Sufficient strength is required in the brace to prevent buckling.

Fences that cross low places can be "pulled down" through use of a deadman or rock buried in the lowest spot. Fasten a wire to the fence above and around the deadman or rock. This will hold the wires down in the low place. The post on either side of the low place should be braced like an end post, using a horizontal brace and diagonal wires. Where fences cross a deeper place, a separate fence should be constructed in it. Or, if water flows in it, self-cleaning floodgates should be used.

Diameter varies with plant size.

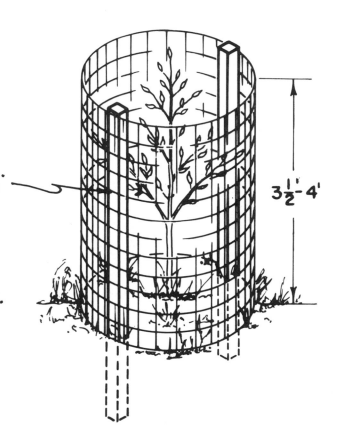

2"x 2" Redwood stakes or 1" steel angle posts. Stakes may be located either on inside or outside of wire.

1" or 2" wire mesh best. Larger mesh or poultry netting can be used.

$3\frac{1}{2}'-4'$

Individual cage for protection from deer and livestock.

Constructing individual cages around young trees or vines may sometimes be more economical than fencing an entire field. A satisfactory cage can be fashioned by forming a 1½- to 2-foot circle of 2-inch poultry or stucco mesh (though 1-inch is preferable); this should be 3½ to 4 feet high and can be supported by two grape stakes.

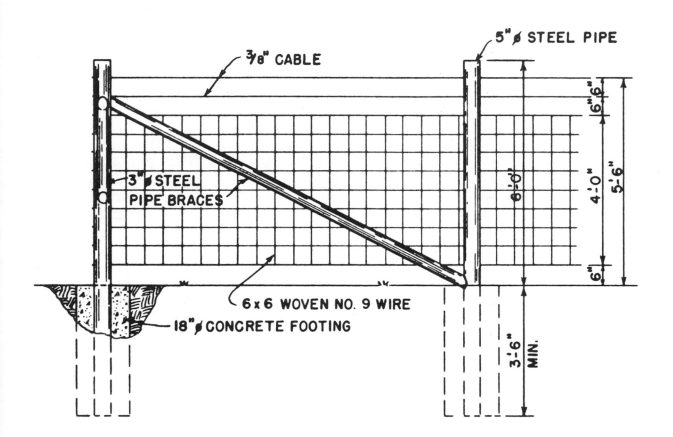

3/8" CABLE

5" ∅ STEEL PIPE

3" ∅ STEEL PIPE BRACES

6 x 6 WOVEN NO. 9 WIRE

18" ∅ CONCRETE FOOTING

6"

6'-0"

4'-0"

5'-6"

6"

3'-6" MIN.

Elevation of fencing typical corner.

Wooden posts or lighter steel may be used to economize.

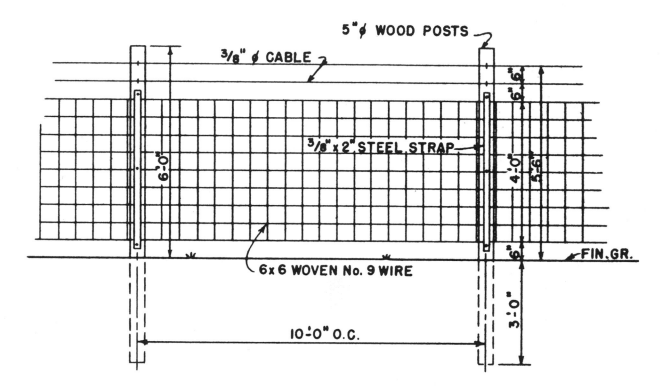

Elevation of typical wire fence.

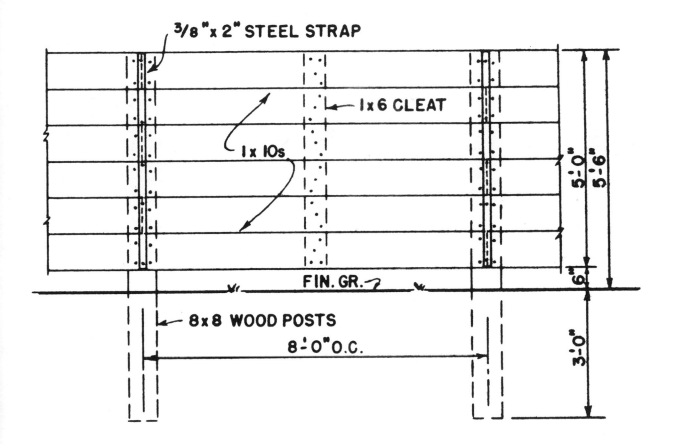

Elevation of typical solid wood fence.

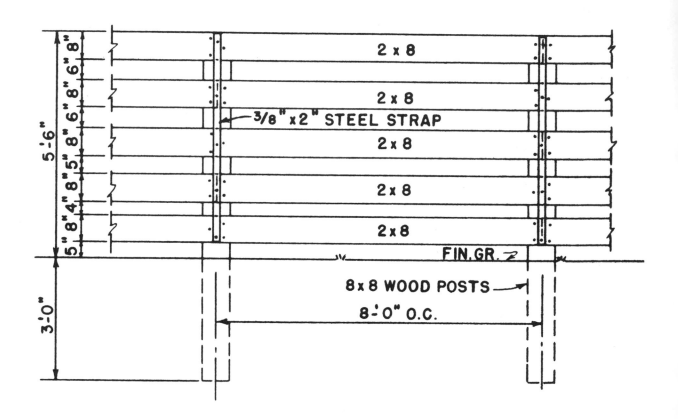

Elevation of typical open wood fence.

A fence as heavy as this would be used only for a bull pen or similar site where extra strength is needed.

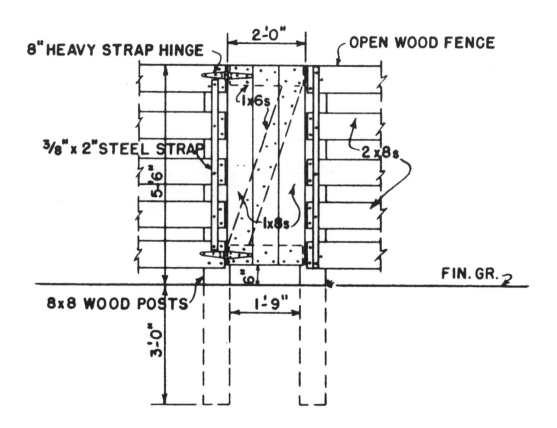

8" HEAVY STRAP HINGE

2'-0"

OPEN WOOD FENCE

1x6s

2x8s

3/8" x 2" STEEL STRAP

5'-6"

1x8s

FIN. GR.

8x8 WOOD POSTS

1'-9"

3'-0"

Solid wood gate for chutes or for human entry.

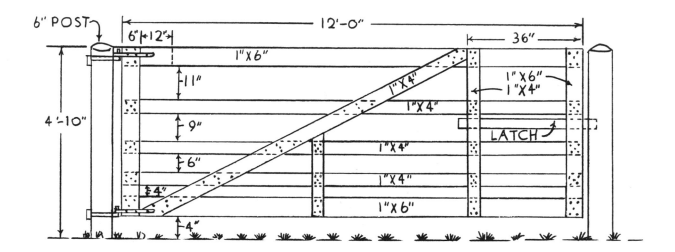

Swing gate.

The same design may be used for any width by simply shortening or extending the length of rails and adjusting braces accordingly.

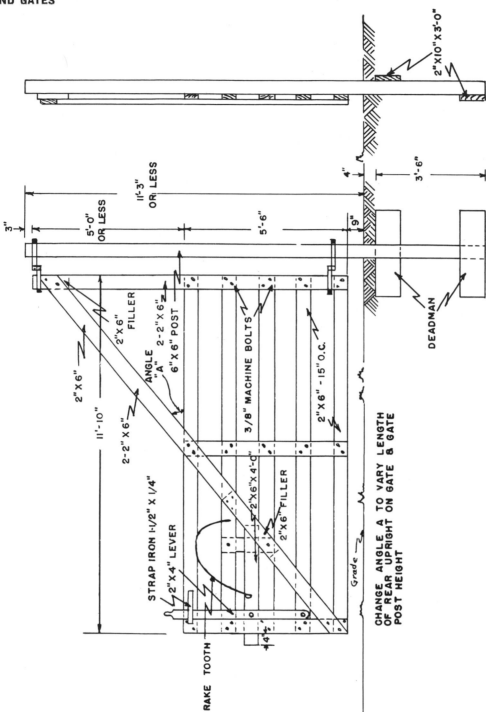

Corral gate.

Some persons prefer that one side of the gate be completely flat or smooth. If this is desired, place all braces on one side and use 4 x 4 end pieces notched out for the rails. (University of Wyoming Circular 148)

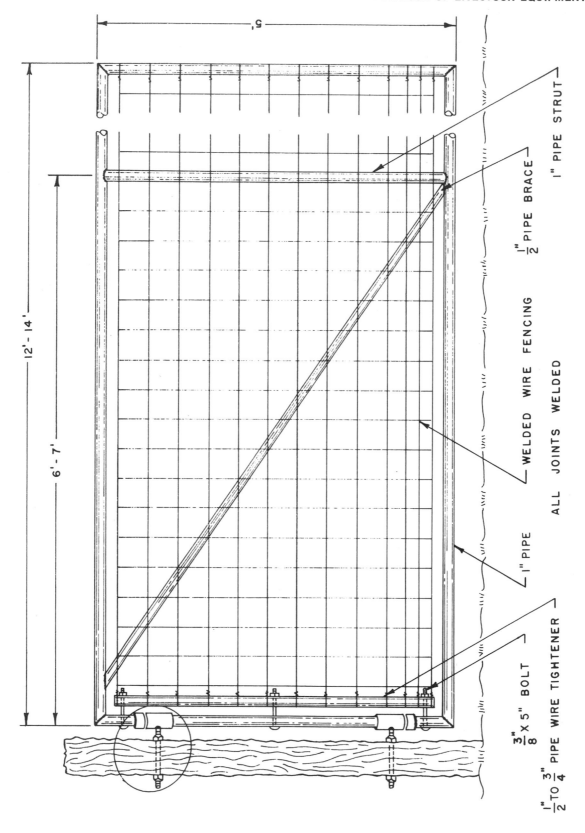

Metal gate.

This gate is made from pipe and covered with heavy netting. Weld all joints securely.

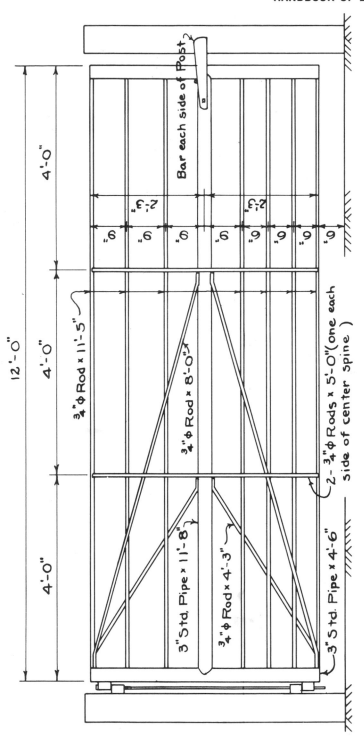

All-welded steel farm gate.

Pump rod, old pipe, or angle iron can be used as well as a variety of new steel of any desirable size.

a. SIMPLE ONE-SPAN BRACE

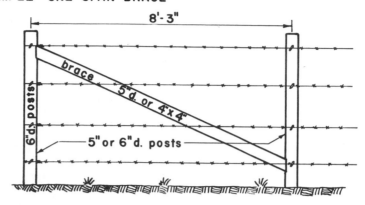

b. DIAGONAL BRACE WITH WIRE TIES

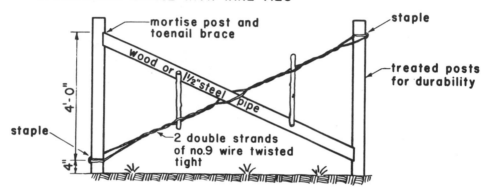

c. DOUBLE SPAN HORIZONTALLY BRACED

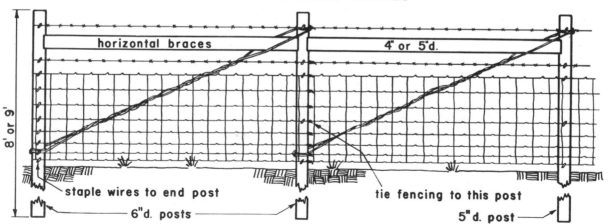

Fence bracing.

To prevent sagging and to keep fence taut it is very important to have the end and corner posts solidly braced. Occasionally trees or other natural barriers may be so located that they can serve as anchor posts, but most of the time they are so out of line it is best to develop one or more corner posts or ends as shown.

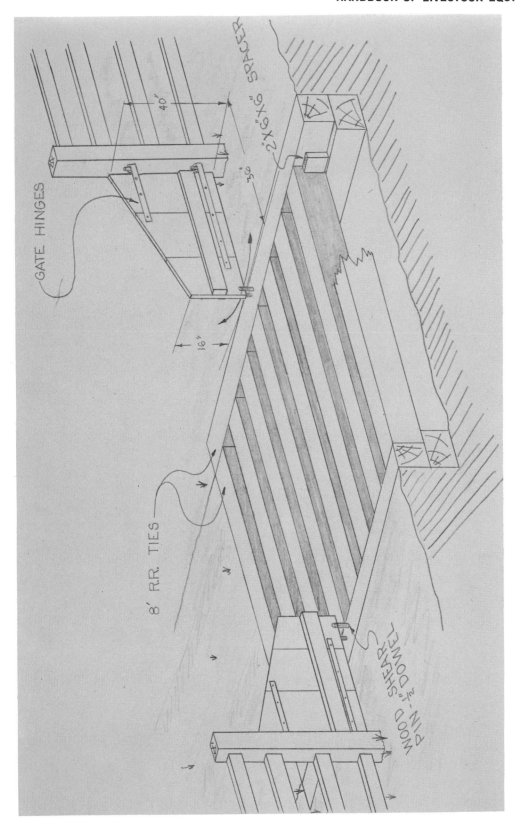

Cattle guard.

This guard is constructed of old railroad ties or similar-size timbers. The depth of the pit is determined by the thickness of the ties or timbers as illustrated. All boards resting on soil must be creosoted or treated. If ties are used no cuts need be made as standard-length 8-foot ties are a standard width for most vehicles. Ties or timbers can be lifted out individually should one or more become damaged, or to clean out the pit of trash or material washed in. Painting the top of the timbers a light color will improve their effectiveness in deflecting livestock.

The swinging gates are designed to swing open for wider vehicles or to let livestock pass through. In case of vehicles hitting the gates the dowel pins will shear and let the gate swing open undamaged.

Whenever possible cattle guards should be located away from turns so vehicles cross them at exact right angles.

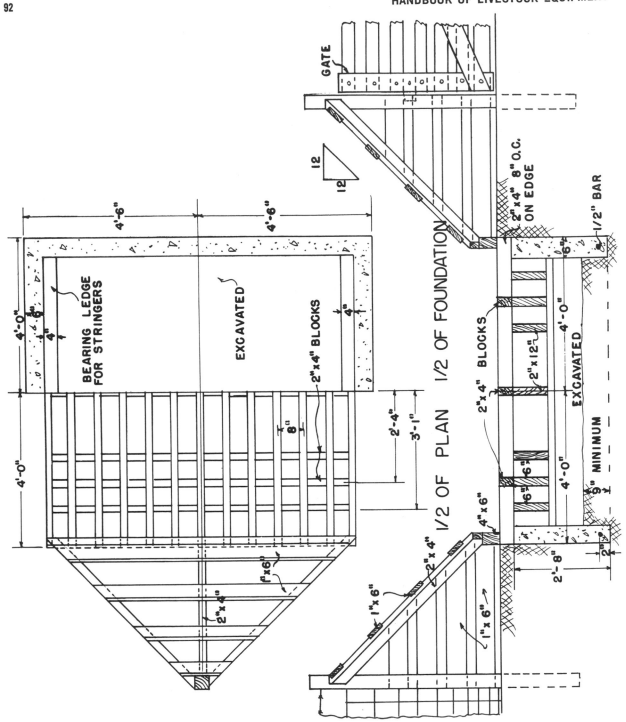

Cattle guard.

Wood, concrete, steel, or combinations of these may be used to build cattle guards. They should be located on straight runs of the road and where it is level or else material will wash in and fill the pit up during winter. (University of Wyoming Circular 148)

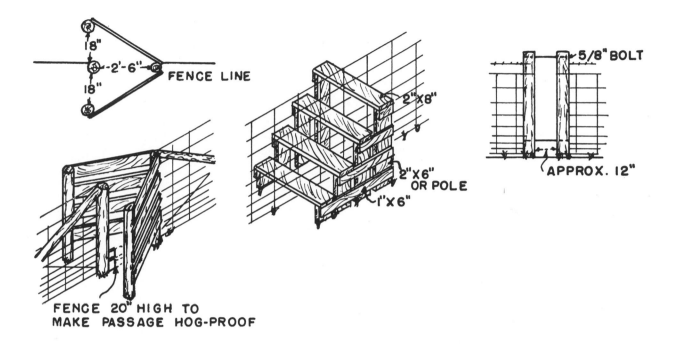

Fence steps and escapes.

Safety in handling cattle is important. Escapes through fences should be provided. In tightly boarded chutes or pens, holes should be left at close intervals for toeholds to allow your hasty exit.

These escapes also let you get back and forth from pen to field without climbing over. They become a convenience as well as a protection.

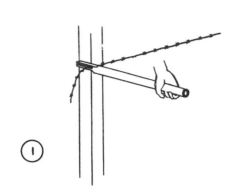

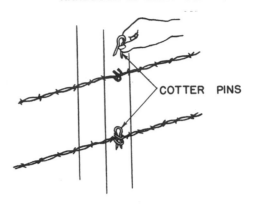

TEMPORARY   FASTENERS

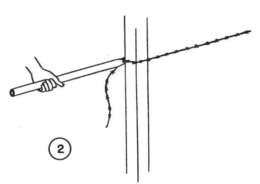

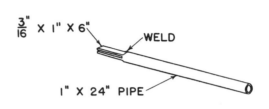

BARBED — WIRE   STRETCHER

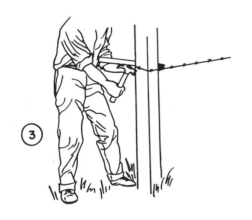

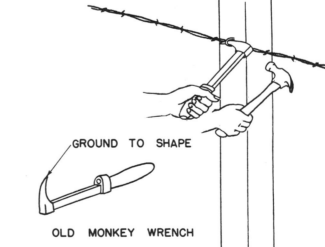

STAPLE   PULLER

Fence repair.

Make fence repair easy by using a few shop-made tools.

1. Two staples and a cotter key or third staple make a good temporary fence. Frequently such fences are used in snow country and lowered to the ground during the winter.
2. Weld two pieces of steel to a pipe handle, leaving enough space for wire, and it will result in a handy fence stretcher.
3. Grind the head of an old monkey wrench to a point to make a good staple puller.

(University of California Extension Service)

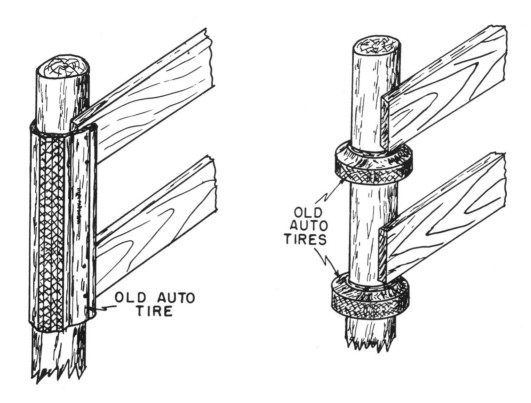

Preventing bruises and injuries.

Millions of dollars are lost each year in bruises and injuries to animals. Some of this loss can be prevented by padding sharp corners and openings through corral fences. There are many ways to do this. Old tires are easily adapted to such protection. The drawings illustrate two ways in which they may be used. Using a wood rasp on corners and driving all nails in level with the surface of timber will also help.

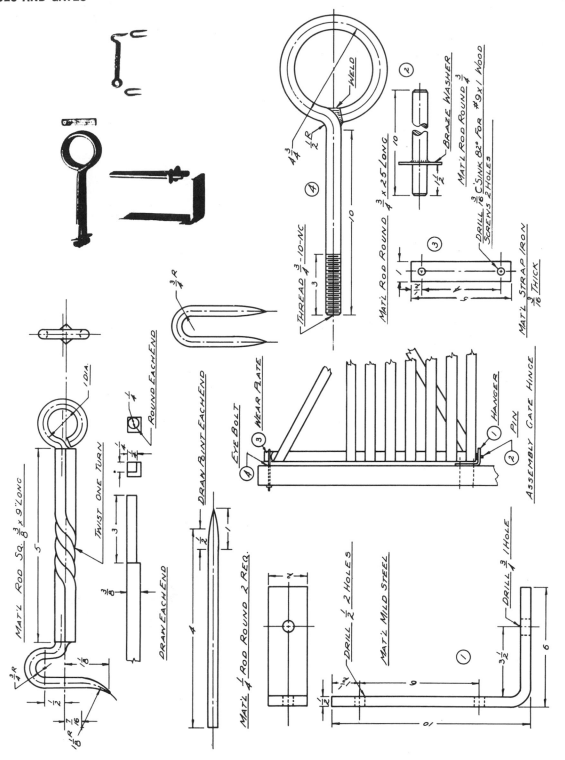

Simple gate hardware.

All of these items can be made in the shop with a forge or torch.

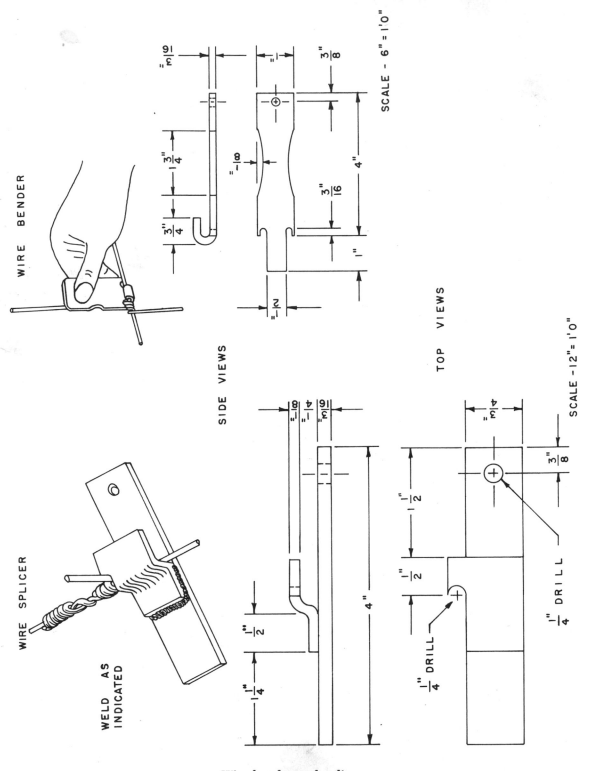

Wire bender and splicer.

These handy tools not only save time but give a very neat and professional look to splices.

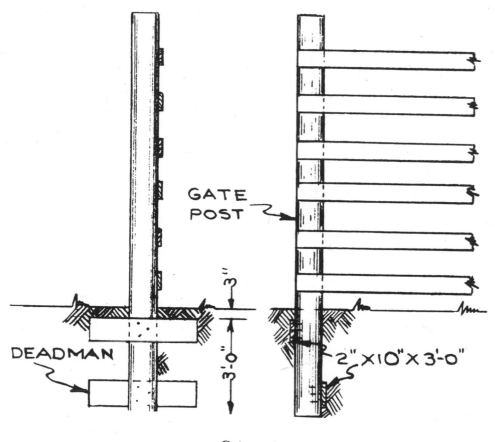

GATE POST

3"

3'-0"

DEADMAN

2" X 10" X 3'-0"

Gate post.

Gate posts should be treated with a wood preservative and should either be set in concrete or have "deadmen" nailed onto the section that goes into the ground. Two-by-tens, 3 feet long, make good material for deadmen.

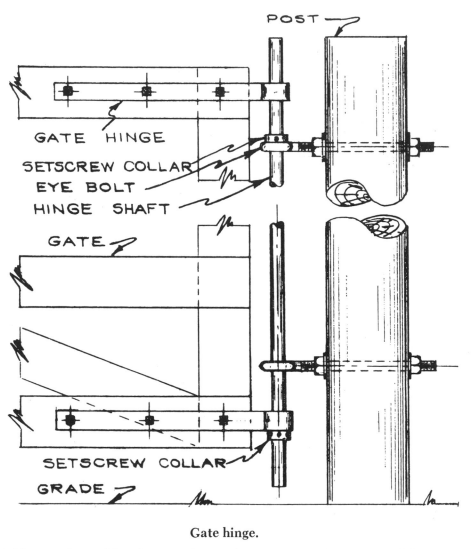

Gate hinge.

An adjustable gate hinge like the one shown above permits the gate to slide upward over the top of packed snow. Such a hinge saves moving snow in areas of heavy snowfall or in spots where snow drifts in to clog the gate.

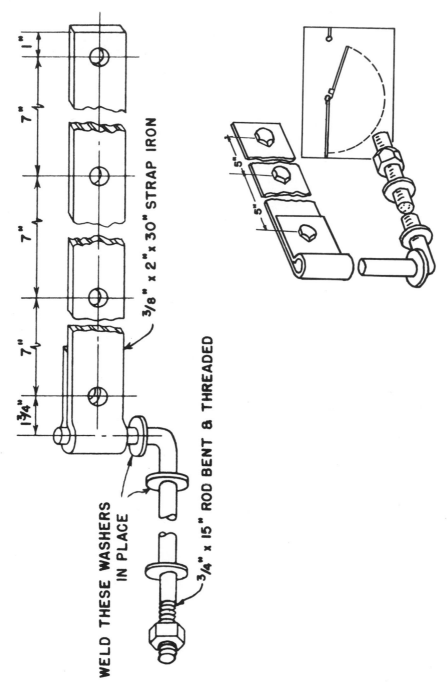

Strap hinge.

The strap hinge is improved if the lug is a bolt rather than a lag screw. A bolt threaded all the way provides more adjustment and often is needed to hang the gate plumb. These hinges can be purchased in a variety of weights, or any hardware store can order them with extra long bolts. Turning one lug bolt over is perhaps the best way to prevent the gate from being lifted off its hinges by livestock.

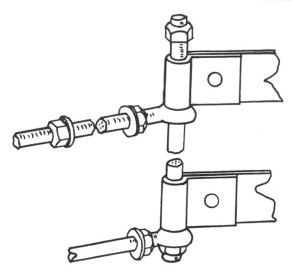

Eye bolt hinge.

This type of eye bolt and continuous rod arrangement is excellent for corral gates. The eye bolt should be threaded all the way and have nuts at each end. If posts are crooked, this arrangement will allow for necessary correction. Eye bolts usually have to be made according to the situation and need.

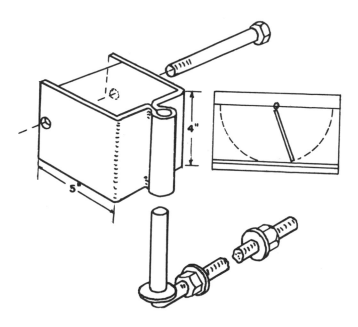

Gate hinge.

This type hinge is excellent where 4" x 4" uprights are used to support the gate. It is best where the gate has to swing 90 degrees each way from its closed position. This type is usually made to order by a machine shop. It can be made with a torch and large vise.

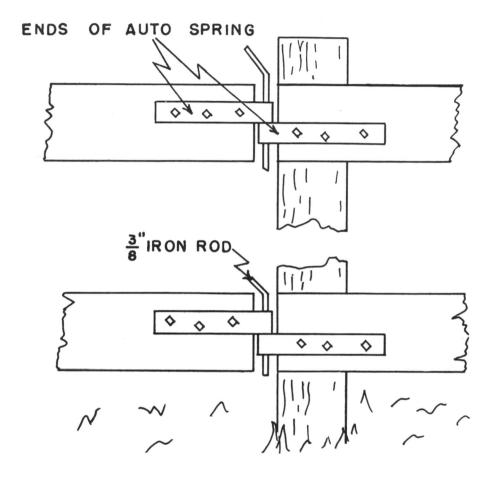

Gate hinge.

This gate hinge is simple and economical. The ends of two automobile springs are used for the hinge. A 3/8-inch or larger rod passes through the holes for the hinge pin. Heat the metal and allow it to cool before drilling the holes in the hinge.

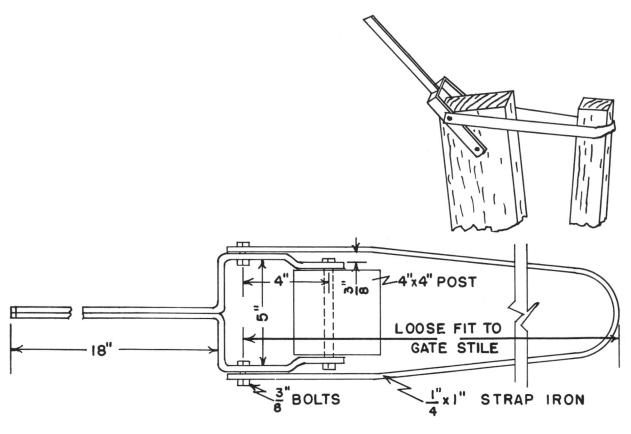

Gate fastener.

This gate fastener is simple to make and is very effective when used on wire gates. It provides a quick, easy way to keep gates tight.

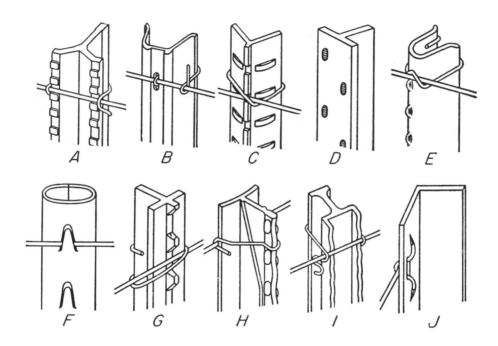

Steel farm fence posts, showing typical shapes, wire binders, and surface treatment.

Shapes or forms: Angles, C and J; Y-form, A; tees, D, G, H, and I; channel or U-bar, B and E; circular, F. Binders: Twisted wire, C; staples, D and J; slip on, G and I; clip and twist, A, B, E, and H; lipped, F. Surfaces: Studded, C and G; embossed, A, C, and E; channelled, A, B, and I; perforated or punched, B, D, and J.

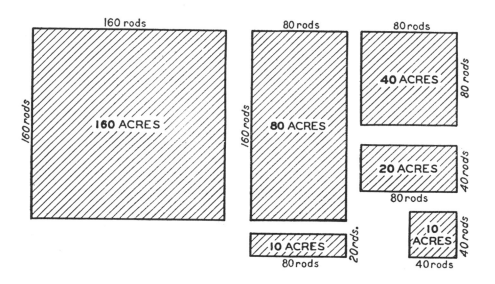

The length of fencing required per acre varies with the size and shape of the fenced area.

NUMBER OF LINE POSTS REQUIRED AT VARIOUS SPACINGS FOR 100 RODS OF FENCING[1]

Post Spacing	Number of Posts	Post Spacing	Number of Posts
(ft.)		(ft.)	
8	205	20	83
10	165	25	66
12	138	30	55
14	118	40	42
16½	100	50	33

1. Corner and gate posts are additional.

Chapter IV

CHUTES AND CORRALS

Well-planned chutes, loading chutes, pens, yards, and other devices make the handling of livestock easier, save labor, and help prevent accidents. They are an asset in maintaining the health of the herd. They are invaluable for the veterinarian and frequently make the more or less routine management procedures of marking, dehorning, horn branding, and general inspection for injuries, parasites, etc., a good deal easier. Money spent on good equipment is a must for the practical handling of livestock.

University of Maryland Extension Service and Washington State University have some good advice regarding requirements for satisfactory corrals and chutes.

1. **Height** at least 5½ feet (6 or 6½ feet for horses or wild cattle).
2. **Strong construction.** Planks or strong poles; closely spaced, heavy posts, set at least 2½ feet in the ground; gates and corner posts 3 feet. Ample bracing; bolts instead of nails at points of strain.
3. **Gates.** Braced for strength and to prevent sag; free swinging. Gate posts "tied" across top above height of a rider. Quick, sure fastener (eye bolt and chain with hook shown). Strong, free turning hinges.
4. **Sorting arrangement.** More than one pen, and a sorting gate. (Two types of sorting gates shown: a 12-foot alley with gate to cut cattle "by" or into pen, such as is used at most public stockyards; and a positive 3-way sort operated from above with a stop gate to control movement of the cattle.)
5. **Chute** to confine cattle for observation, branding, spraying, etc.
6. **Smooth** inside surface to prevent bruises.

Other desirable features are:

1. **Easy entrance.** Corral in corner of pasture. Line fence poled or planked out 5 to 10 rods. "Wing fence" 5 to 10 rods long at an angle from end of gate back into pasture.
2. **Easy movement of cattle.** Corners rounded where cattle are crowded. Fence poles or planks close enough that cattle can't get legs through. Solid sides of chute to prevent climbing. Gradual crowding of cattle to chute. Gates hinged at the end to "follow" and crowd cattle. Corral near level (cattle move up a slight grade more easily than on level or down hill).
3. **Chute.** At least 20 feet long for fast handling. Base narrow (not over 1 foot), sloping out to 30 inches at belly height.
4. **Squeeze.** To hold cattle for dehorning, branding, etc. Side-opening style faster than end opening.

5. **Loading chute,** opening on good road.
6. **Dipping vat,** with return leading to holding pen.
7. **Proper size.** Herds up to 40 or 50 cows handled in corral 60 x 72. Larger pens and chutes required for larger herds.

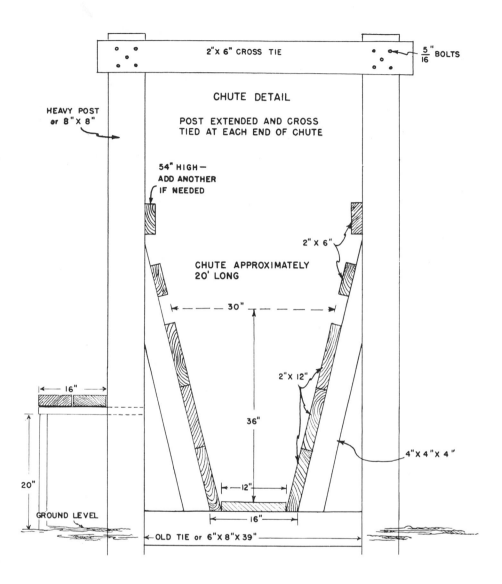

Cross section of chute.

Posts in ground should all be treated. It is important to maintain minimum measurements in order to prevent livestock from turning around inside. (Washington State University Extension Service)

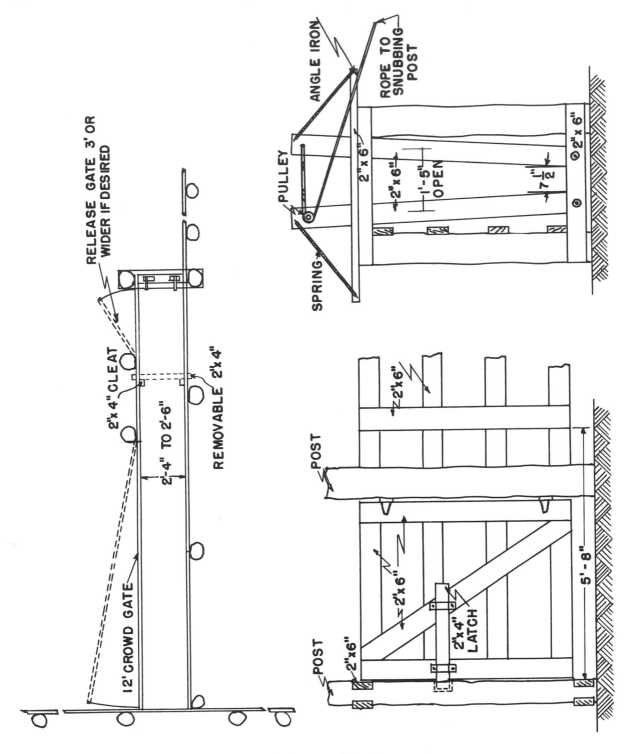

Livestock chute and headgate.

The measurements are for cattle but can be used for sheep or swine as well by reducing width and lowering to a more suitable height.

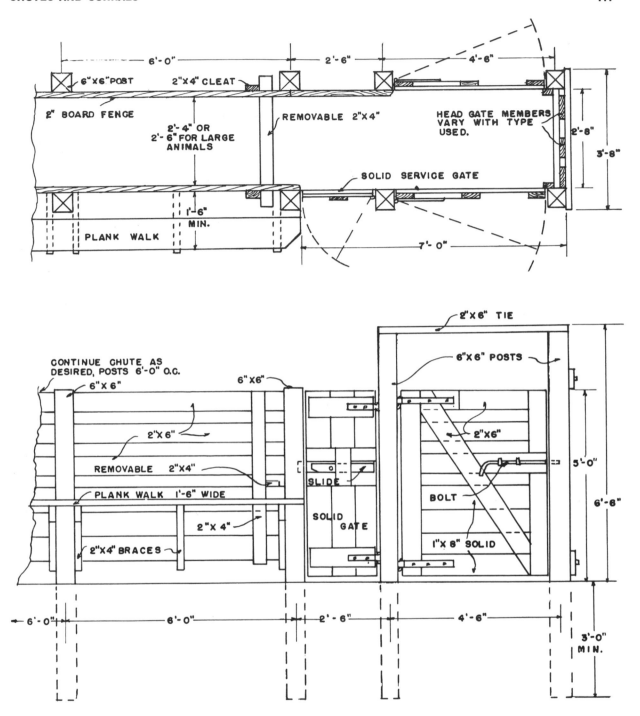

Cattle chute.

Either a commercial or shop made headgate or branding chute may be placed at the end if the built-in headgate is not used. (University of Wyoming Circular 148)

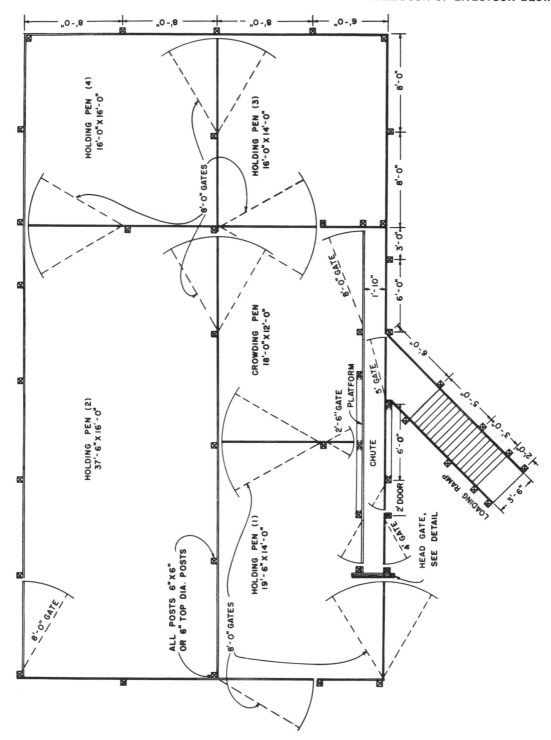

Holding chute and corral.

A simple holding chute easy to construct with new or used lumber. Cross ties should not be omitted if chute is to retain its shape under heavy usage. (Continued on next page.)

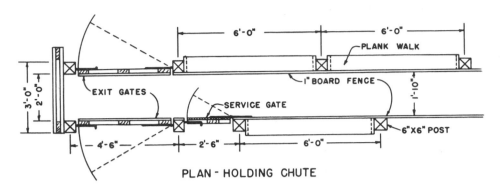

PLAN - HOLDING CHUTE

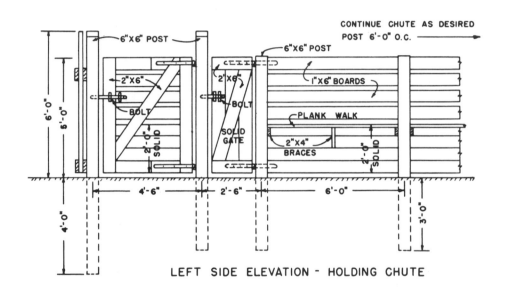

LEFT SIDE ELEVATION - HOLDING CHUTE

Holding chute and corral (continued).

Basic unit consists of chute, loading ramp, crowding pen and holding pen (1). Next addition for a more complete unit would be holding pen (2). For more pens add (3) and (4).

Sturdy and conveniently arranged holding pens, chute, and loading ramp can be a real labor saver in safe and efficient handling of cattle. One or two men can handle cattle safely and easily in facilities similar to the one illustrated. Adaptions may be made in this layout to fit individual farm conditions. Every livestock farm should have these facilities.

The corral should be located on a well-drained site convenient to pasture fields and to an all-weather road. A location in the corner of a field makes it easier to drive cattle into the pens. Pens adjacent to barns permit use of some of the shelter for holding pens. Cattle usually can be driven more easily into pens they have been accustomed to using.

Plank fences leading to the corral 40 to 50 feet adjacent to it permit easier corralling of the cattle. (Plan C-5. 24, Virginia Polytechnic Institute)

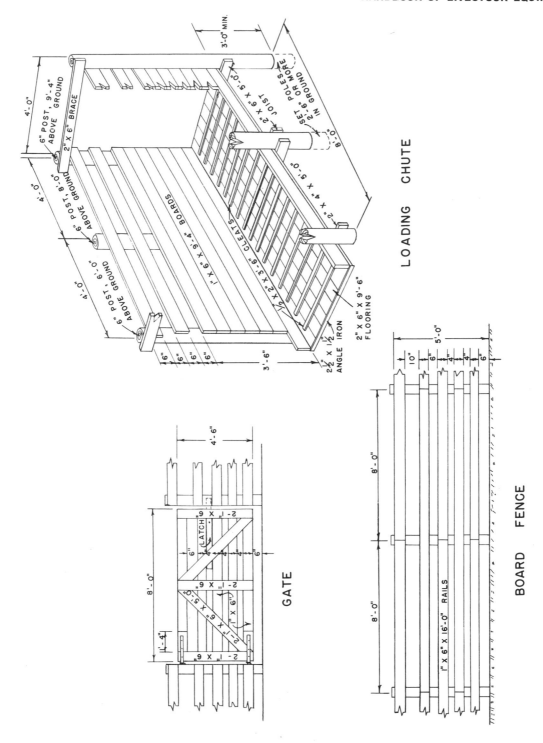

Loading chute and corral gate.

Steps or solid concrete may be used as flooring if desired.

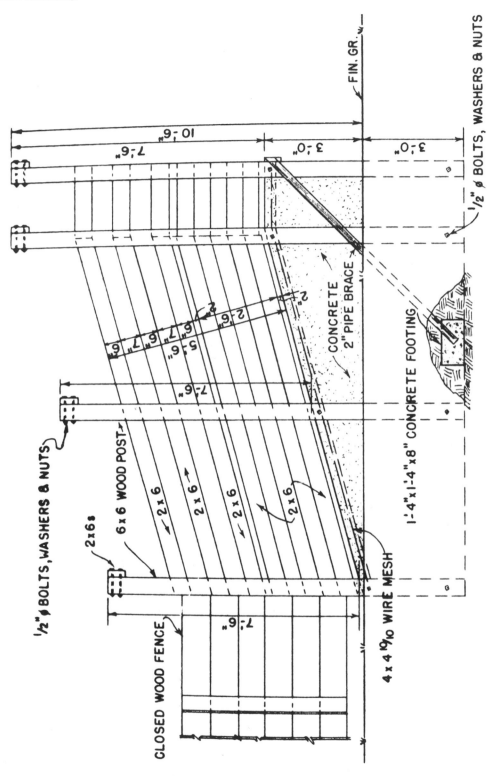

Side view of loading chute.

If sturdy, treated posts are used the pipe brace and concrete footing may be eliminated.

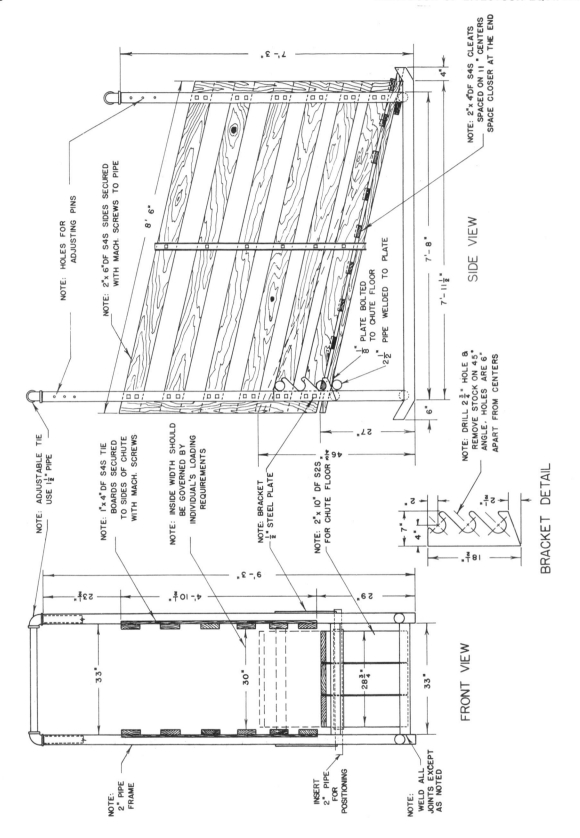

NOTE: HOLES FOR ADJUSTING PINS

NOTE: 2" x 6" DF S4S SIDES SECURED WITH MACH. SCREWS TO PIPE

NOTE: 2" x 4" DF S4S CLEATS SPACED ON 11" CENTERS SPACE CLOSER AT THE END

7' - 3"

8' - 6"

4"

7' - 8"

7' - 11½"

6"

⅛" PLATE BOLTED TO CHUTE FLOOR

2½" PIPE WELDED TO PLATE

SIDE VIEW

NOTE: ADJUSTABLE TIE USE 1½" PIPE

NOTE: 1" x 4" DF S4S TIE BOARDS SECURED TO SIDES OF CHUTE WITH MACH. SCREWS

NOTE: INSIDE WIDTH SHOULD BE GOVERNED BY INDIVIDUAL'S LOADING REQUIREMENTS

NOTE: BRACKET ½" STEEL PLATE

NOTE: 2" x 10" DF S2S FOR CHUTE FLOOR

27"

46½"

NOTE: DRILL 2¾" HOLE & REMOVE STOCK ON 45° ANGLE. HOLES ARE 6" APART FROM CENTERS

BRACKET DETAIL

7"

4"

2"

2"

1½"

1½"

18⅞"

FRONT VIEW

9' - 3"

23¾"

4' - 10½"

29"

33"

30"

28¾"

33"

NOTE: 2" PIPE FRAME

INSERT 2" PIPE FOR POSITIONING

NOTE: WELD ALL JOINTS EXCEPT AS NOTED

Portable loading chute.

Note that the height may be adjusted for any size truck bed by relocating the pipe on the plate.

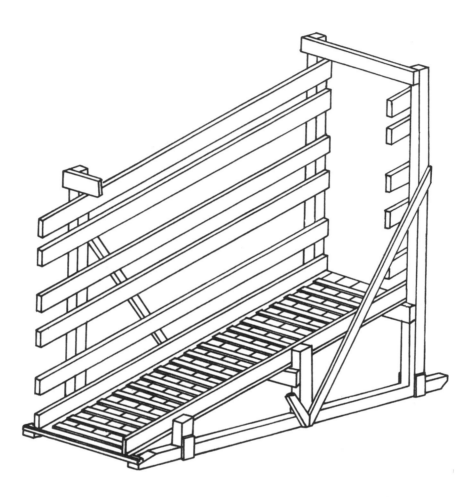

Cutaway section of a simple loading chute that can be skidded to new locations as needed.

Sides and ties should be 2 x 6 or wider with 4 x 4 posts.

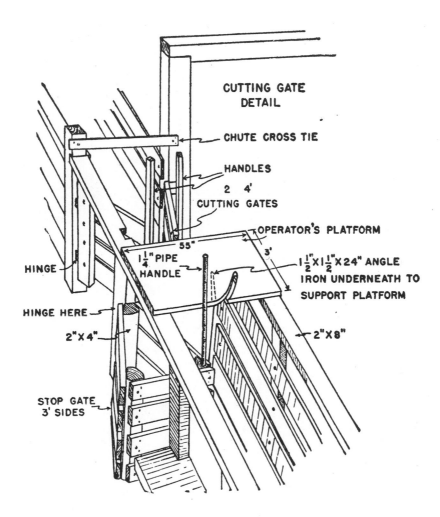

CUTTING GATE
DETAIL

CHUTE CROSS TIE

HANDLES

2 4'
CUTTING GATES

OPERATOR'S PLATFORM

55"

1 1/4" PIPE
HANDLE

3'

1 1/2" X 1 1/2" X 24" ANGLE
IRON UNDERNEATH TO
SUPPORT PLATFORM

HINGE

HINGE HERE

2" X 4"

2" X 8"

STOP GATE
3' SIDES

Cutting chute design for cattle or sheep.

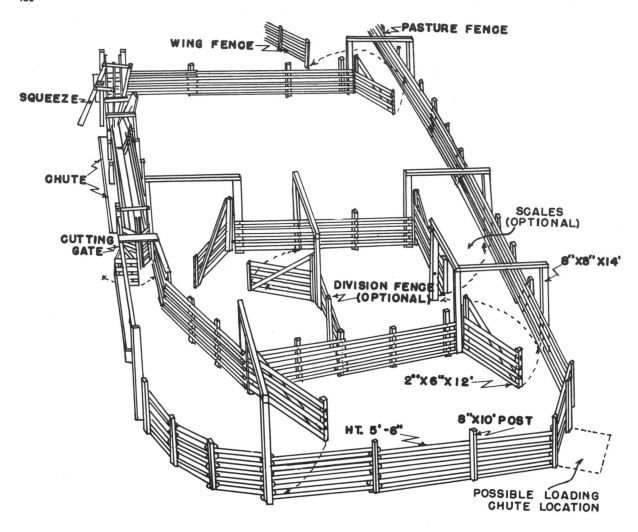

Corral and chute arrangement.

A chute, equipped with a suitable head gate for holding cattle, is a key piece of equipment. No one plan is best for certain features, but construction details will help you develop an arrangement best suited to your situation.

The chute should be located away from the loading chute. It should be arranged so the large gate at the end can be used as a deflector, along with the corral fence, to get the animals into the chutes. How a gate is used is shown on one of the plans for chutes and head gates. An approach to the cattle chute often is built in the form of a "V" and used as a crowding pen.

The chute leading from the pens to the head gate should be about 30 feet long, to accommodate four or five animals. This length will prevent delays for the veterinarian; it can also speed up jobs like dehorning and, in general, allows best use of available help.

The chute should be not more than 30 inches wide. Some herds can be accommodated in a 28-inch chute. Young stock are less likely to turn around in the narrower chute. When working calves, some cattlemen use a panel fastened to one side of the wide chutes commonly used for larger cattle. The panel uses 2" x 4" or 2" x 6" smooth timbers. (University of Wyoming Circular 148)

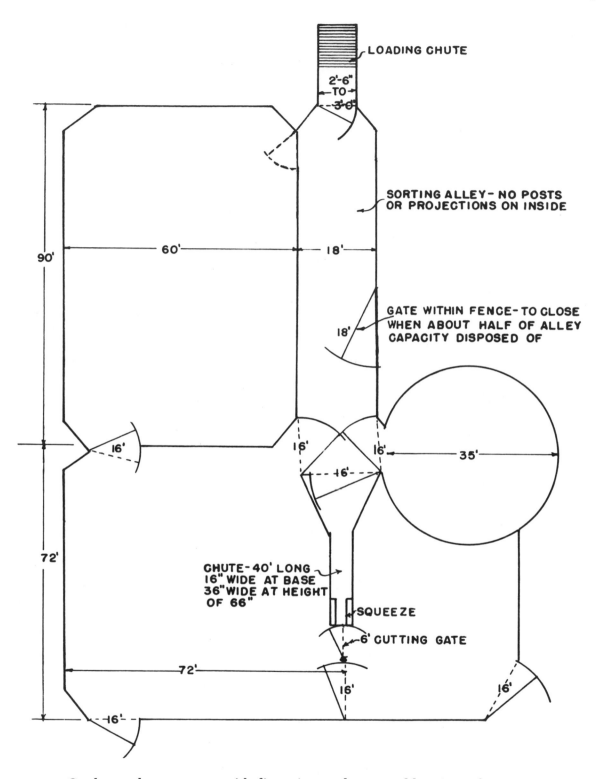

Cattle corral arrangement with dimensions and suggested locations of gates.

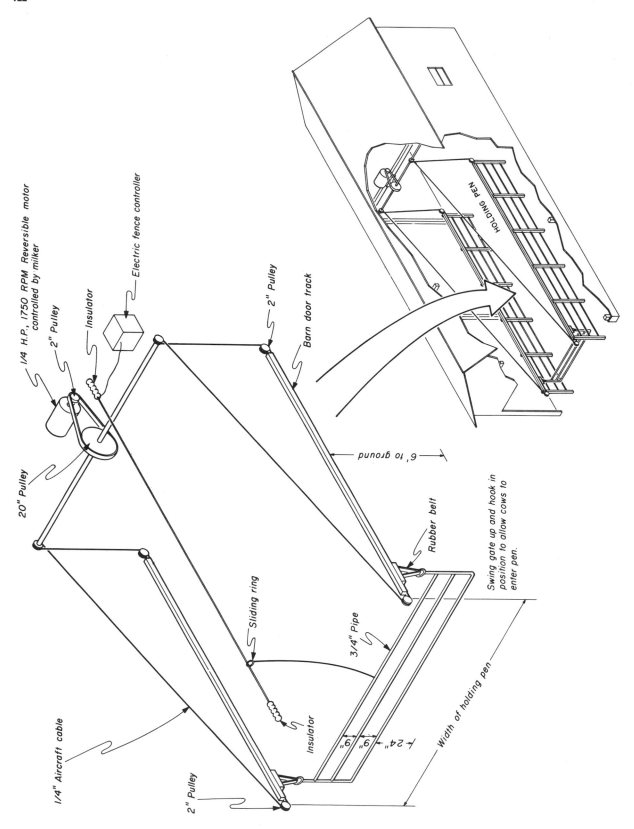

1/4 H.P., 1750 RPM Reversible motor controlled by milker

2" Pulley

Insulator

Electric fence controller

2" Pulley

Barn door track

HOLDING PEN

20" Pulley

6' to ground

Rubber belt

Swing gate up and hook in position to allow cows to enter pen.

Sliding ring

3/4" Pipe

1/4 Aircraft cable

Insulator

2" Pulley

9"   9"   24"

Width of holding pen

Dairy crowding gate.

The crowding gate shown in this plan has been successfully used by many dairies. As the illustration indicates, it is used to move cattle away from the fence and toward the milking parlor. The secret is the lightweight design and the electric fence charger that "persuades" cattle to move. After the cows become accustomed to the gate, the fence charger is seldom needed. A dimmer control can be used to reduce the shock intensity. The unit is controlled by the milker, and an additional control can be placed at the entrance to the holding pen. Since the units move rapidly, care should be taken not to overcrowd the animals. A stop should be placed at the end of each track. (OSA 241, Agricultural Extension Service, University of California, Davis)

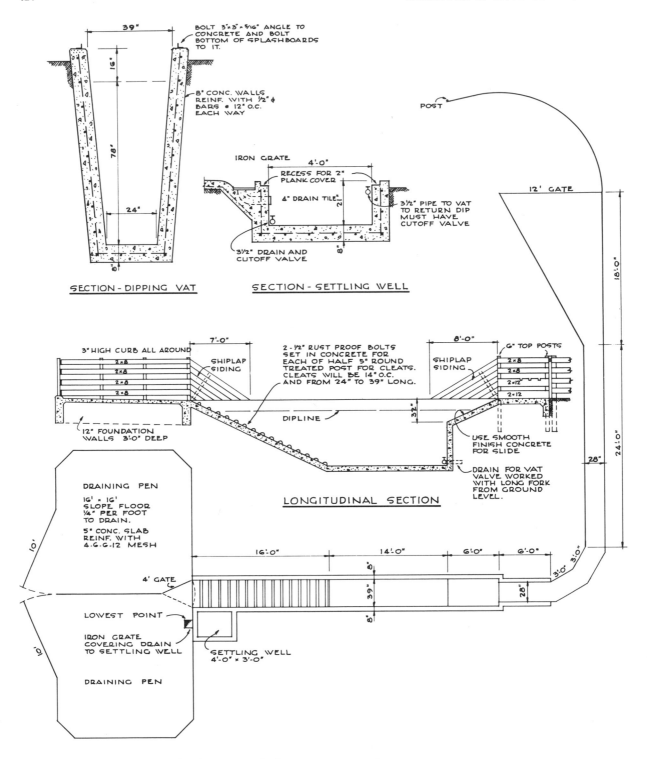

Dipping vat with draining pens and approach gate.

Some ranches use spray-type equipment, but dipping vats are still used on many larger ranches. They are trouble-free, once constructed.

Chapter V

LOADING AND TRANSPORTATION EQUIPMENT

The items of equipment shown in this chapter are presented merely as ideas and suggestions. They represent workable equipment which has proved satisfactory, and it is hoped that they may serve as guides for you in planning and equipping your farm or ranch.

It has been said many times that good equipment makes a good farm or ranch better. In these days of scarce and high-cost labor it would seem that practical, workable equipment which will enable cattle to be handled more easily and quickly, and with less waste in labor, time, and feed, is of essential importance for any producer or feeder of cattle. Then, too, visitors and customers are impressed not just by the cattle, but by the methods, the equipment, and especially the fences they see. Surely it is just good business to see that your visitors and customers are favorably impressed.

Loading equipment and transportation equipment are among the first items that visitors and customers see when they visit your ranch. Furthermore, one animal killed or injured during loading or moving may cost more than any of the equipment needed to properly handle the animals.

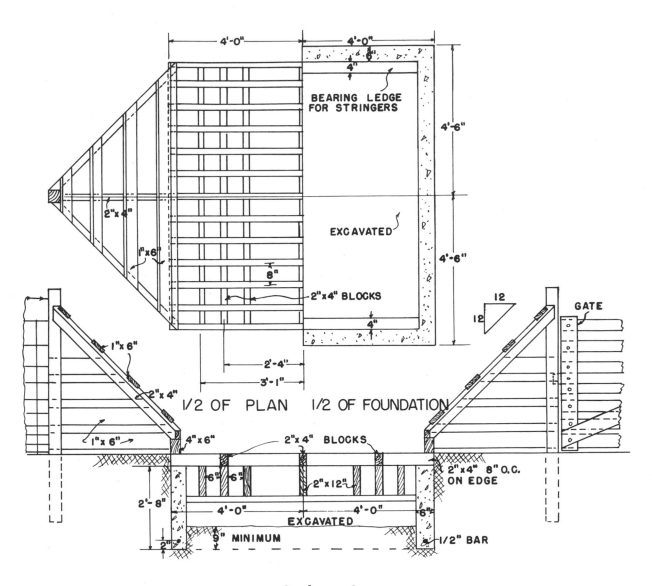

Cattle guard.

Either wood or concrete can be used in construction of this cattle guard. A gate should be provided on the side for livestock to pass through when needed.

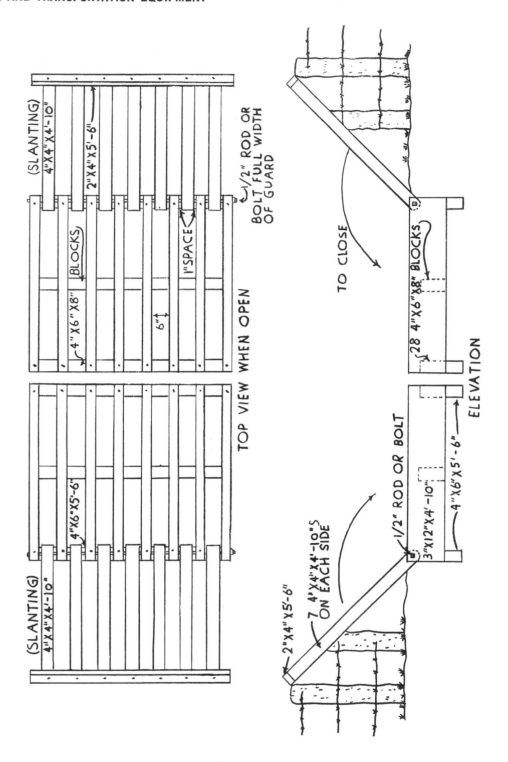

Collapsible cattle guard.

An important feature of this cattle guard is that the side will fold in, allowing either vehicles or livestock to cross it if desired. (Montana State University)

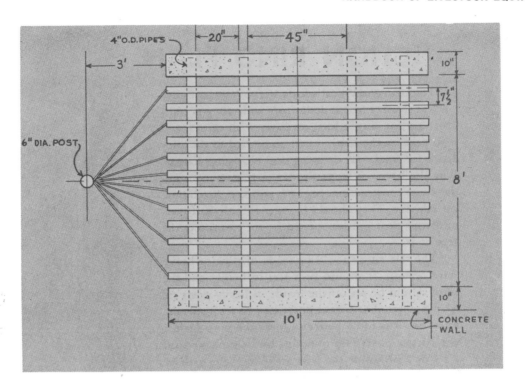

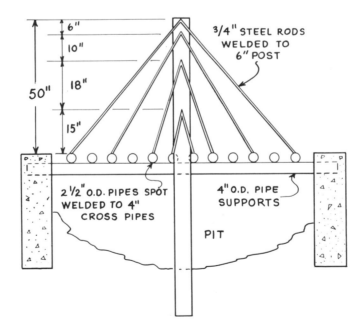

Pipe cattle guard.

This guard of rod and pipe construction is standing up well and is easy to build. The open ends make it easy to clean when it blows full of trash and the heavy 4-inch pipe supports are satisfactory. In some cases, the cross pipes are set down about ½ inch in the 4-inch pipe cross supports in order to obtain more welding surface.

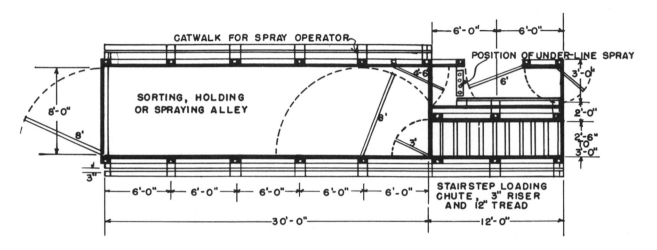

Holding alley.

A holding alley is used for sorting, holding, spraying, and loading. The sides of the alley should be made of planks or poles to give a smooth surface. Alleys will vary in length according to the number of cattle usually handled at any one time. A spray alley 8 feet by 30 feet will hold a carload of cattle crowded closely together; this prevents runoff of spray material from their backs. At the end of the alley is a loading chute and to one side an underline spray setup. A plan for a compact alley for the average corral is shown here. These suggestions for a holding alley are easily modified and adapted to the needs of the individual farm and ranch. (Colorado State University)

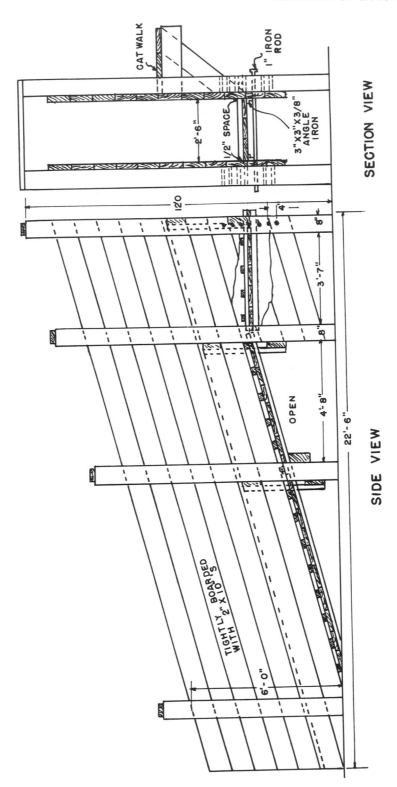

Adjustable loading chute.

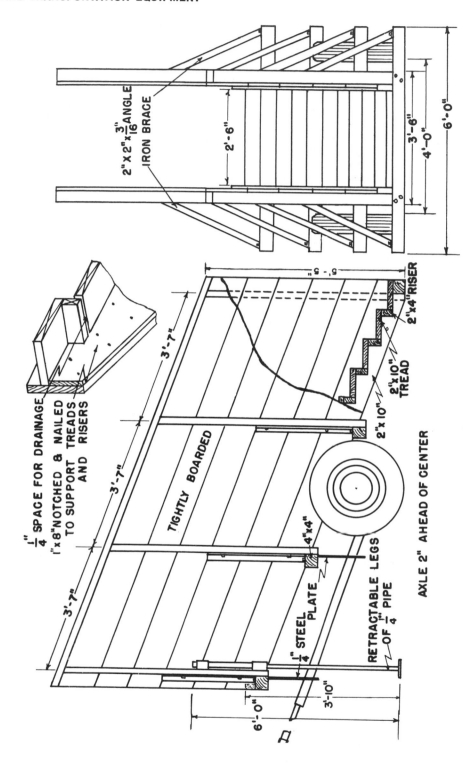

Portable loading chute (stair-step type).

Cattle seem to go up stairs as well as they do a ramp and seldom slip or fall.

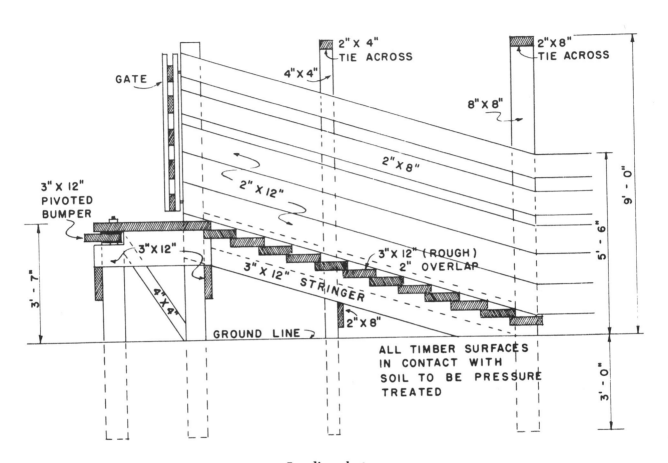

Loading chute.

The step-type loading chute is rapidly gaining in popularity. Here is a drawing for such a chute made of squared lumber. This chute is in use on the campus at Washington State University. It makes use of a pivoted bumper and adjustable wing gates. With its 12 steps, it rises 3 feet, 7 inches.

The treated posts might be round timbers, but the other parts would be easier to assemble if made from rough-sawed lumber.

In general, the width depends upon individual conditions, and whether you prefer to load one animal at a time or several at once. If the steps are made wider than the 3 feet shown, it would be well to put another stringer in the center of the steps. Another set of short posts is necessary to support this stringer.

Check with the trucker who usually hauls your stock to determine the best height for your chute. Then you may add or subtract steps to make the chute fit your own needs.

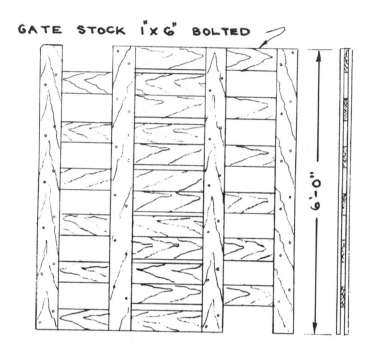

GATE STOCK 1"x 6" BOLTED

6'-0"

Telescoping wing gate.

A telescoping wing gate is a desirable feature to build into the loading chute. Various stop locks may be used to hold wing gates in position when in use; a pointed iron bar works well.

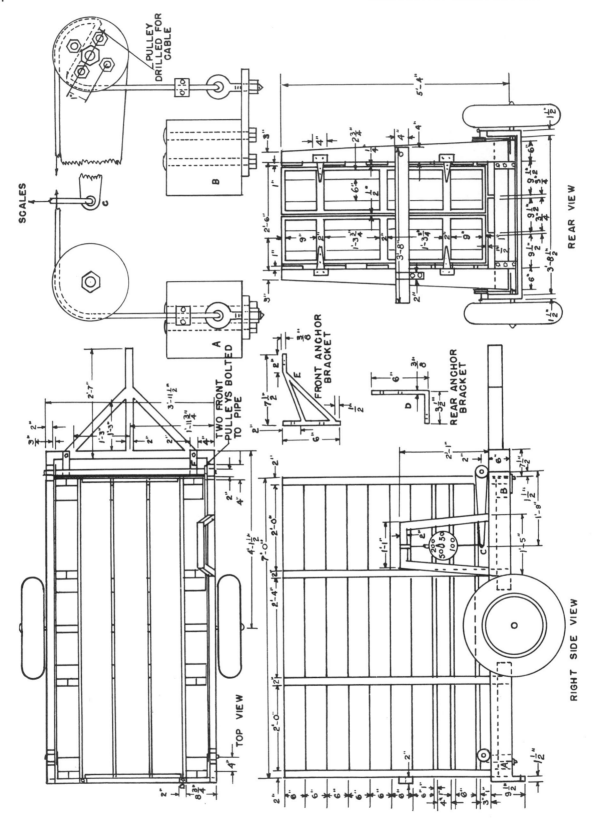

Portable livestock scale.

A scale is an important piece of equipment on a livestock ranch. It should be located where it can be used quickly and easily but where animals can be worked around it without having to pass over it unless desired. (University of Wyoming Circular 148)

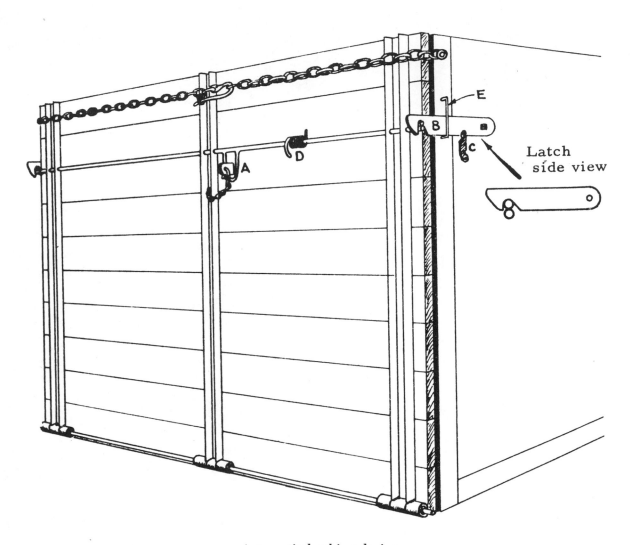

Automatic latching device.

Most latching devices also need some kind of permanent way of securing doors or gates during transportation.

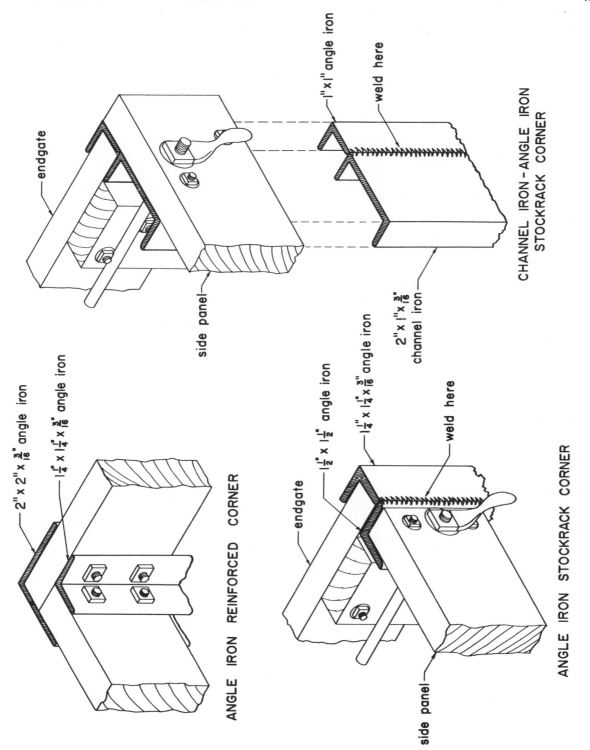

Corner reinforcement.

Stock racks will not vibrate open during transport if the corners and edges are secure.

Chapter VI

RESTRAINING EQUIPMENT FOR LIVESTOCK

Anyone who has attempted to handle livestock will agree that proper equipment to subdue animals so they can be treated when sick or worked on to perform usual livestock practices is essential. It is not only necessary so the tasks can be performed quickly and easily but imperative for the safety of both operator and animal. Typically, many ranches do not have equipment to do the job of restraining animals, or else it is in poor repair. Excellent commercial equipment is available but it is expensive, and most of the equipment can be readily made at home with used material (lumber and steel from the scrap pile) found around the ranch. Many ranches can adapt and improve on items they build so they are even better than the original plans. However, measurements are critical, so size of openings, etc., should be rigidly followed.

Restraining equipment is found in other chapters of the book, so if what is needed is not here, check the Index.

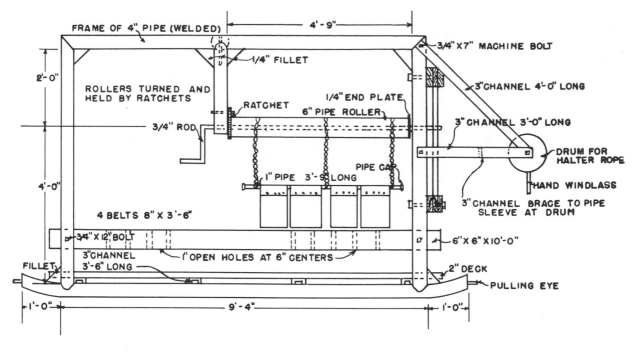

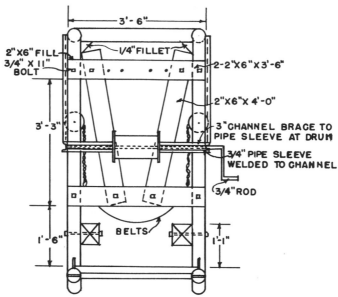

Portable cattle stock.

Cattle stocks are needed to help in foot trimming, surgery, or other operations. The drum is used to hold the animal against the stanchion.

This chute of pipe and steel, except for the floor and trimming rail, was developed by John M. Lewis & Sons and was first used by them and the Fort Hays Branch of the Kansas Experiment Station. This plan puts the rear posts back out of the way of trimming the hind feet and is liked by all who have tried it. This equipment has the front windlass high enough to keep the animal's head held high, which is important. (American Hereford Association)

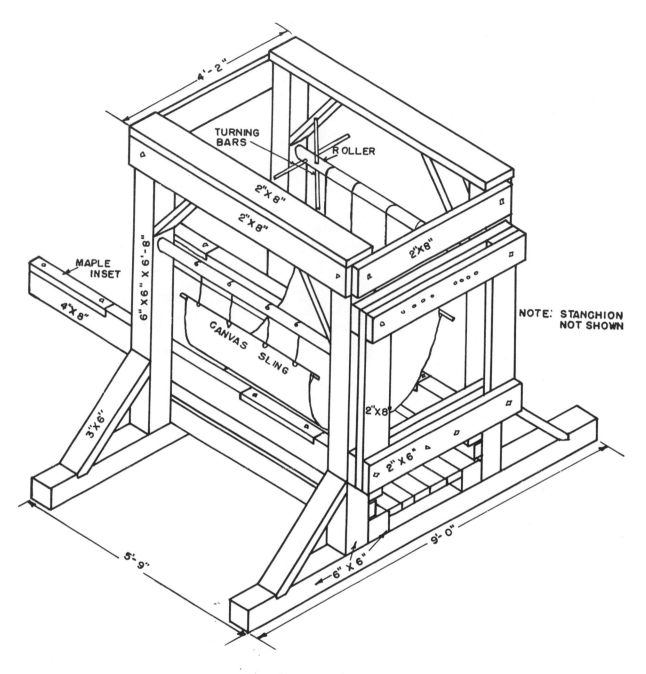

TURNING BARS

ROLLER

2"X8"

2"X8"

2"X8"

4'-2"

MAPLE INSET

4"X8"

6" X 6" X 6'-8"

CANVAS SLING

3"X6"

2"X8"

2"X6"

6" X 6"

5'-9"

9'-0"

NOTE: STANCHION NOT SHOWN

Cattle stock.

Many beef breeding and handling units need a cattle stock to assist in foot trimming, surgery, and other operations.

Some operators prefer a low front so that the front feet and legs can be pulled forward for working. The plan can be readily altered for those who want the low front.

One variation is to use a stanchion to hold the animal.

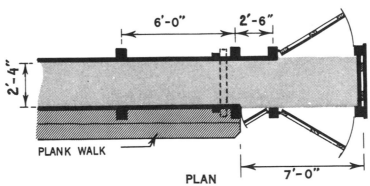

Cattle-holding chute and headgate.

This chute has a catwalk and a small service gate on one side, with exit gates on both sides. Different type headgates, including those manufactured commercially, can be used on the end of the chute.

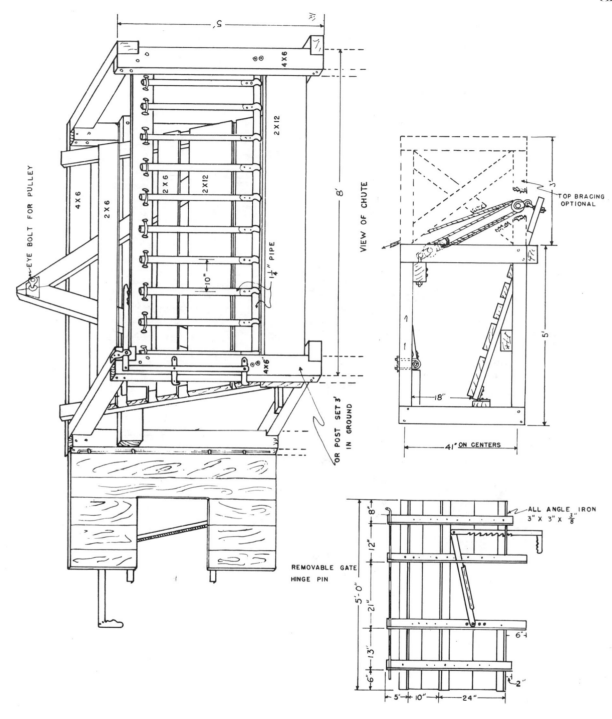

Squeeze chute.

This chute can be made using materials found around any ranch. The swinging headgate has a major advantage when releasing an animal from the chute, as it swings off the animal's neck rather than requiring it to pull its head back through when the gate is opened. The chute could also be adapted to make it portable.

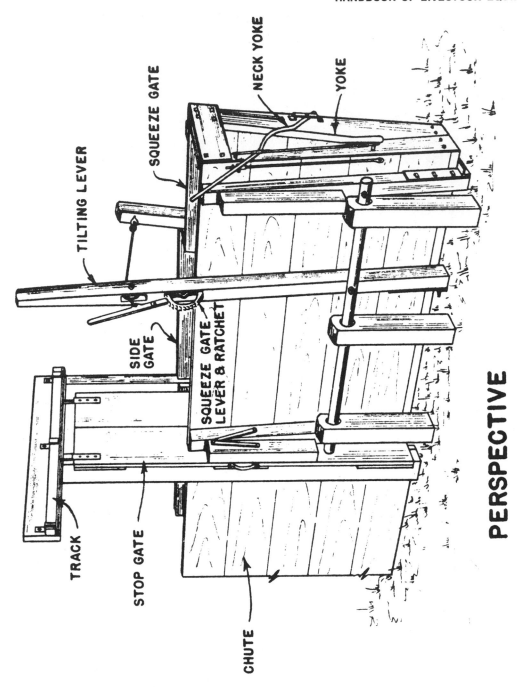

Tilting calf table.

This sturdy proven calf table can be constructed from materials found around the farm or ranch for a considerable saving in dollars. All lumber should be sound and free from knots, especially at critical points. Posts are made of 3" x 3", 4" x 4", or 4" x 6", whichever is available. Sides can be 1- or 2-inch-thick boards or ¾-inch plywood, providing the plywood is protected. See also the following illustration. (Plan 5962, Cooperative Extension, Agriculture and Homemaking, Oregon State University, Corvallis)

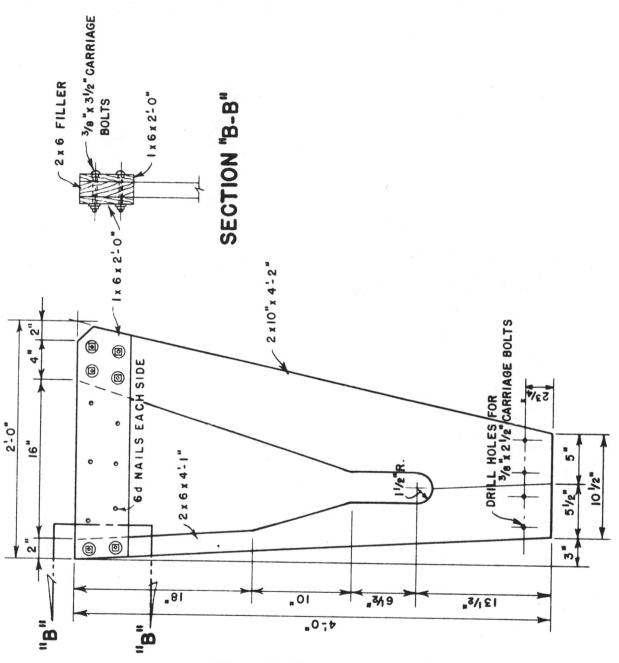

Tilting calf table (continued).

This shows an enlarged section, with dimensions of the squeeze gate. (Plan 5962, Cooperative Extension, Agriculture and Homemaking, Oregon State University, Corvallis)

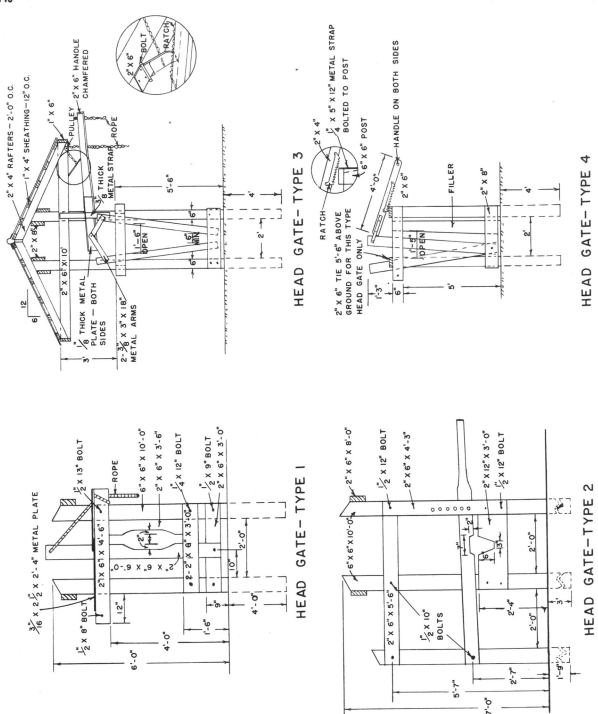

Headgates.

Four types of headgates. Often times all or at least the major portion of livestock operations can be carried on with just a headgate. This would be especially true on a purebred ranch where cattle are gentle, or on a dairy cattle operation.

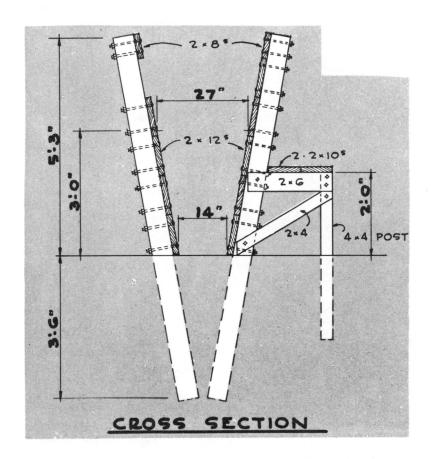

Cattle chute.

This chute, for commercial cattle, is 24 inches wide inside and has a 14-inch working space on the right side. The approach to the chute should always have one straight side. The chute should be long enough to accommodate four or more animals. With posts set on 6-foot centers, each section will accommodate one cow.

A number of breeders prefer the sloping-sided chute. It does accommodate horned cattle nicely, yet is sufficiently narrow at the bottom to prevent young cattle from turning around. The stop bars are inserted from the right side, and work is done from the platform. Since the posts almost meet at the bottom it is much simpler to dig a trench for each pair of opposite posts and set the posts in concrete. A block bolted to each post can be used to stop the cross bars from extending out over the working platform.

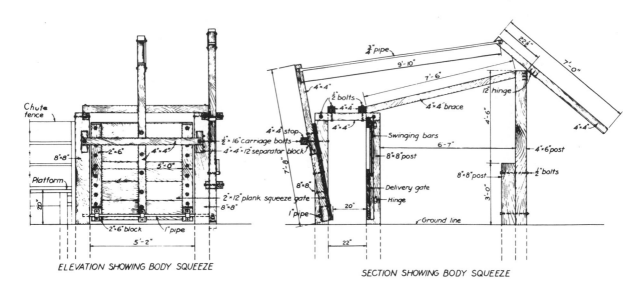

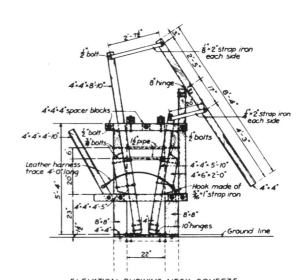

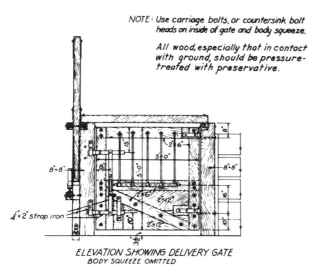

ELEVATION SHOWING BODY SQUEEZE

SECTION SHOWING BODY SQUEEZE

NOTE: Use carriage bolts, or countersink bolt heads on inside of gate and body squeeze.

All wood, especially that in contact with ground, should be pressure-treated with preservative.

ELEVATION SHOWING DELIVERY GATE
BODY SQUEEZE OMITTED

ELEVATION SHOWING NECK SQUEEZE

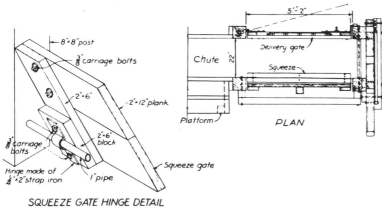

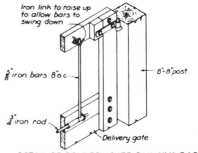

SQUEEZE GATE HINGE DETAIL

PLAN

DETAIL OF DELIVERY GATE SWINGING BARS

Cattle squeeze chute.

Information and plans (detailed) on this and other chutes can be had by contacting the U.S. Department of Agriculture, Agricultural Engineering Research Division, Plant Industry Station, Beltsville, Maryland.

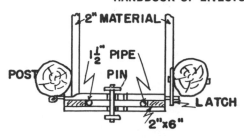

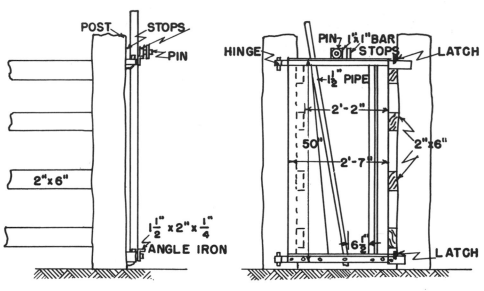

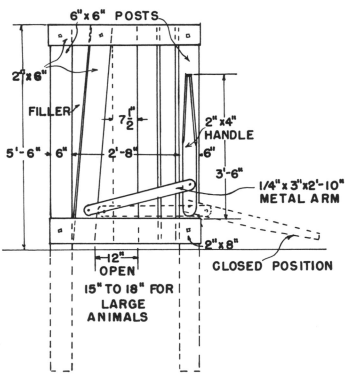

Headgates.

Here are two types of headgates. Note that one swings open from the bottom and the operating handle is out of the way in either position. (University of Wyoming Circular 148)

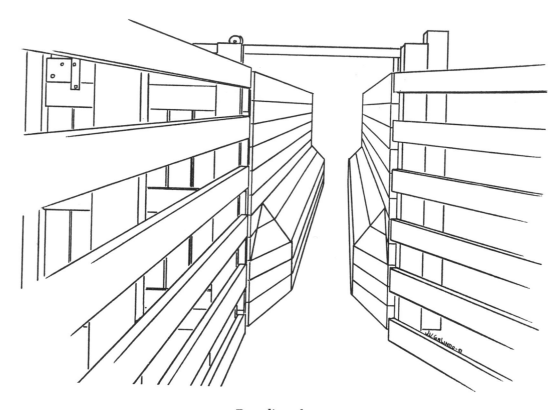

Branding chute.

This view of the chute is toward the entrance end. Note the flared ends near the bottom to guide cattle into the chute and prevent bruising. A squeeze can be set up at the far end.

Walkways are desirable on any kind of chute. Sliding gates should be constructed at either end of the branding chute by crossing 1'' x 6'' 's and nailing them well.

Some cattlemen like to build curved chutes, thinking the cattle will enter them more readily. This type is more difficult to construct and is not so convenient to incorporate in the general corral plan. Most cattle chutes are straight. Cattle usually want to return to the area from which they came, therefore chutes located so that the animals can be driven into them in that direction are desirable. A hoist for raising cattle which may go down in the chute can be set on top of the sides. (Experiment Station, University of California, Davis)

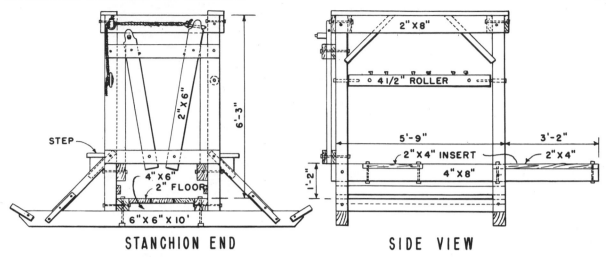

STANCHION END

This view shows a simply designed stanchion. The head holding rails are held in place with pins in the cross rail and also by a rope fastened as shown.

SIDE VIEW

The canvas sling winds up on the side rollers. The 2" x 4" hardwood inserts are bolted for easy replacement after damage caused from trimming hoofs.

TURNING BAR

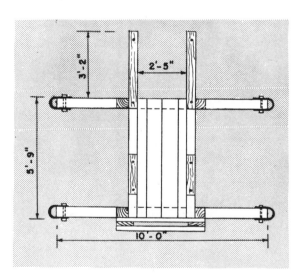

PLAN VIEW

A 2" x 8" plank can be placed on edge across the floor under the stanchion to keep animal's front feet from slipping off front of platform.

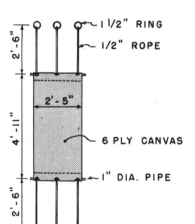

CANVAS SLING

Four bars like the one shown above are usually required for turning the rollers on which the canvas sling is attached. A lug is welded 3" from end of bar.

Cattle stock.

This is an important piece of equipment for handling valuable animals, as it reduces the chance of injury to both man and animals.

Large-scale drawings are available from U.S. Department of Agriculture Miscellaneous Publication 762.

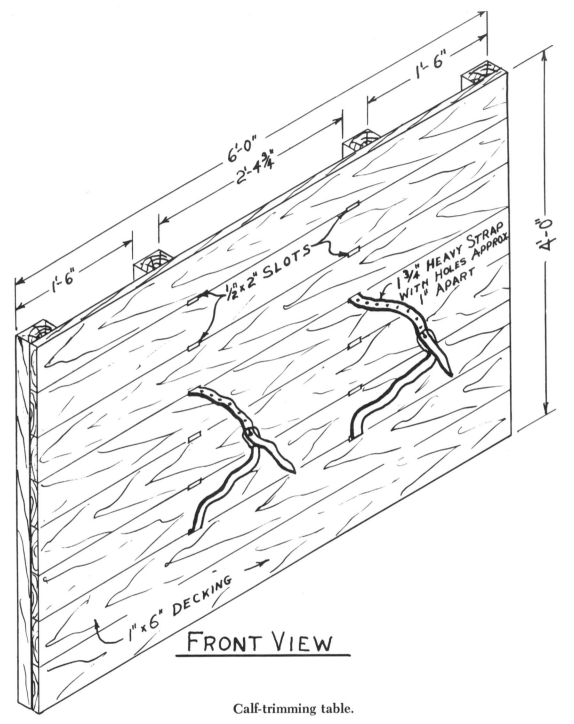

Calf-trimming table.

This table is especially handy for fitting show calves who are used to being handled but have to be kept still in order to be worked on. (Texas A & M University and USDA)

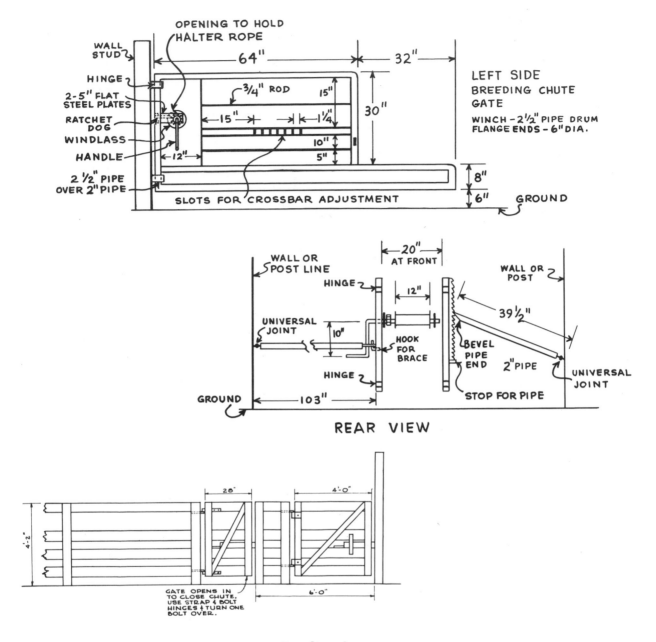

Breeding chute.

A chute developed by John M. Lewis & Sons, Larned, Kansas, which serves the dual purpose of hand breeding and artificial insemination. A winch helps pull the cow forward and the side which swings out helps in getting the cow in position quickly.

A walk-in gate (for handlers) just behind the working section of the chute has proved to be very handy on many ranches. This gate, when open, closes the chute, and it is not impractical to have this section of the chute covered. (American Hereford Association)

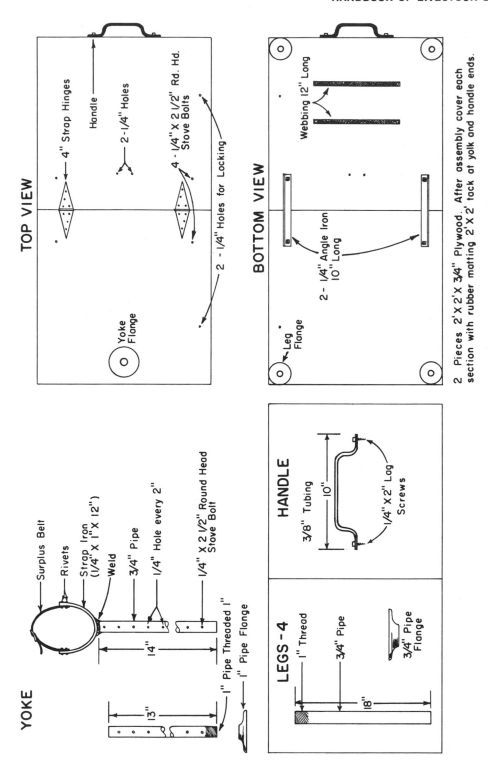

Folding sheep-trimming table.

This device is very handy to take to fairs and shows, as it is easily folded and reassembled.

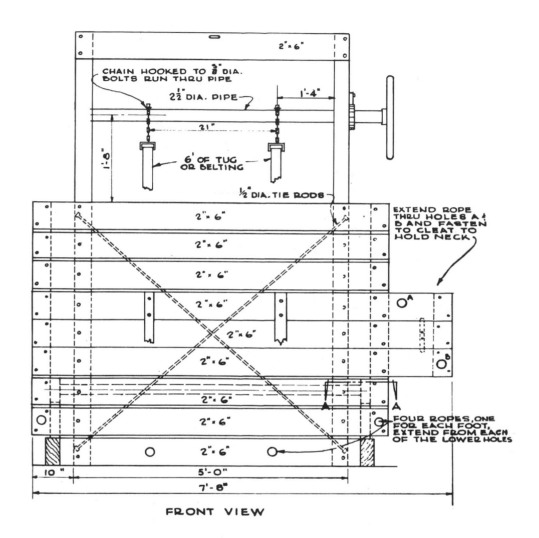

Tilting-table stocks.

In using this equipment, tie the feet of the animal with 3 to 6 inches of rope. The neck, not the head, is secured by a rope coming from hole B, passing over the neck, and through hole A. A center section of an old car spring, or a specially made moon-shaped piece of 2" x ¼" steel, is effective in holding the rope tightly and securely. The neck rope must not come loose, or horned animals will break a horn. A couple of extra holes in the bottom 2 x 6 will be necessary to accommodate smaller animals. (Continued on next page.)

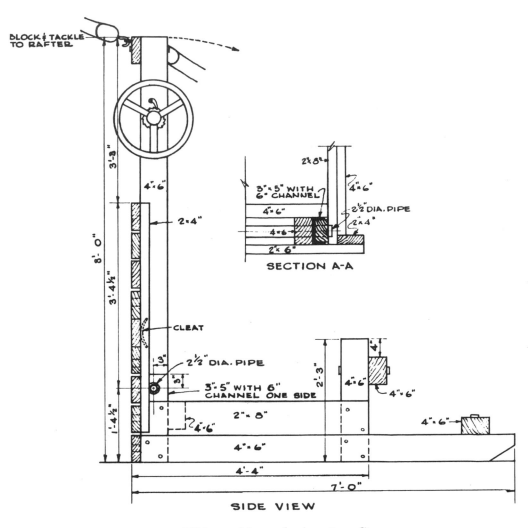

SECTION A-A

SIDE VIEW

Tilting-table stocks (continued).

BILL OF MATERIALS

Quantity	Description
2	4x6—8 ft. table beams (upright)
2	4x6—7 ft. runners
2	4x6—5 ft. 6 in. cross braces
1	4x6—6 ft. cross brace (rear)
2	4x6—2 ft. 3 in. posts (rear)
2	3x5—1 ft. 7½ in. posts for axle
2	2x8—4 ft. 2⅜ in. side bracing
1	2x6—5 ft. top cross tie
3	2x6—7 ft. 8 in. table
5	2x6—6 ft. 5 in. table
1	2x6—5 ft. 6 in. table
1	2½ in. diam. pipe—6 ft. roller
1	2½ in. diam. pipe—5 ft. 10 in. axle
2	6 in. channel iron—1 ft. 7½ in. posts for axle
2	½ in. diam. rods —6 ft. 9 in. tie rods
2	3-6 in. belting—6 ft.
2	chains—3 ft.

(American Hereford Association)

Chapter VII

EQUIPMENT FOR HORSES

Equipment for horses need not be expensive, but it should be sturdy and free of any projections or sharp edges that could cut the animals. Woven wire fences should be avoided; in fact, any wire fence is second choice for fencing horses, although in large fields it often must be used. Poles or 2-inch lumber is best to use in any type of construction, especially on fences or paddocks.

Whenever a woven wire fence is desired, or plans specify its use, it should be of a small-mesh, heavy-gauge wire manufactured especially for use with horses.

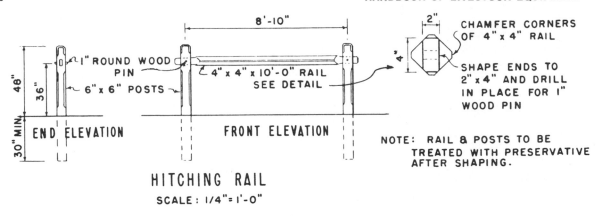

HITCHING RAIL
SCALE: 1/4" = 1'-0"

Hitching rail.

This rack or rail is easy to construct and has a sturdy, rustic appearance. Redwood material is preferable or any lumber which does not have a tendency to splinter. Posts should be set at least 2 feet into the ground and located free from other obstructions, such as water faucets, shrubs, equipment, etc., although shade is desirable if the hitching rack can be located to take advantage of it.

PERSPECTIVE

Riding horse barn.

The overhang is high enough to ride under, and the double door arrangement permits ventilation and allows horse to see out or to be inspected when the lower door only is closed. (USDA Plan No. 5838)

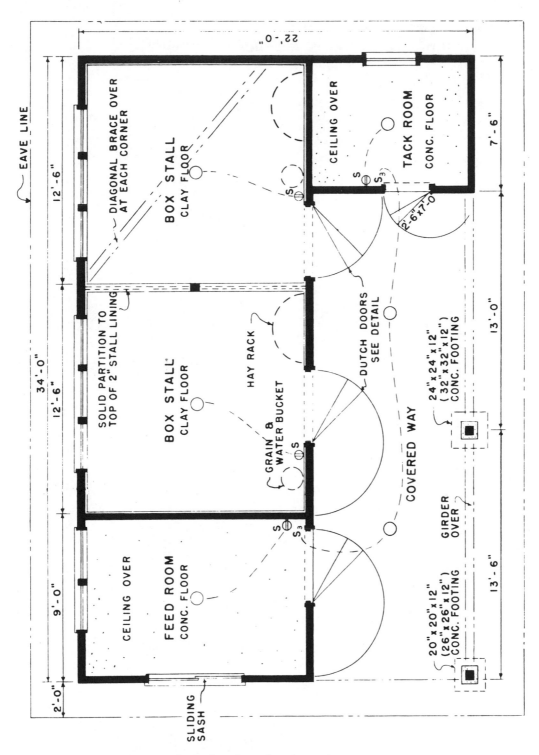

Floor plan for riding horse barn.

Construction costs will vary greatly depending on how finished the structure is, especially on the interior.

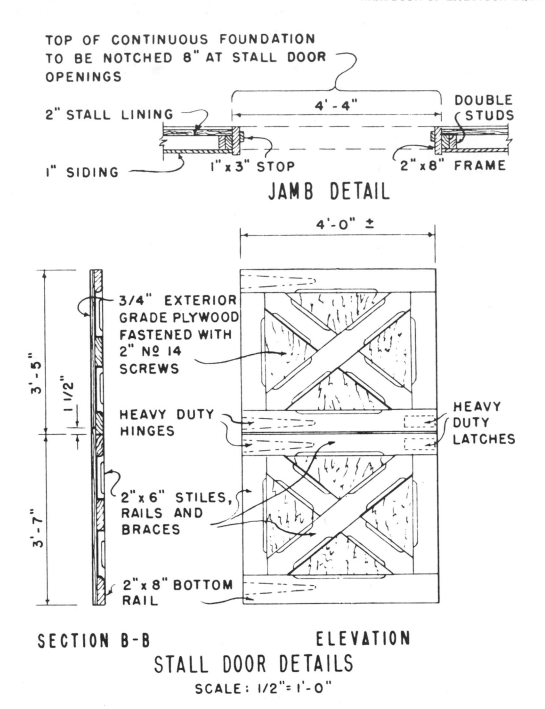

TOP OF CONTINUOUS FOUNDATION
TO BE NOTCHED 8" AT STALL DOOR
OPENINGS

4'-4"   DOUBLE
STUDS

2" STALL LINING

I" SIDING   I"x 3" STOP   2"x8" FRAME

JAMB DETAIL

4'-0" ±

3/4" EXTERIOR
GRADE PLYWOOD
FASTENED WITH
2" Nº 14
SCREWS

3'-5"

1 1/2"

HEAVY DUTY
HINGES

HEAVY
DUTY
LATCHES

2"x6" STILES,
RAILS AND
BRACES

3'-7"

2"x 8" BOTTOM
RAIL

SECTION B-B   ELEVATION
STALL DOOR DETAILS
SCALE: 1/2"= 1'-0"

Double doors for horses.

The doors are a most functional part of any horse barn. They should be strong and neatly constructed to withstand continued use.

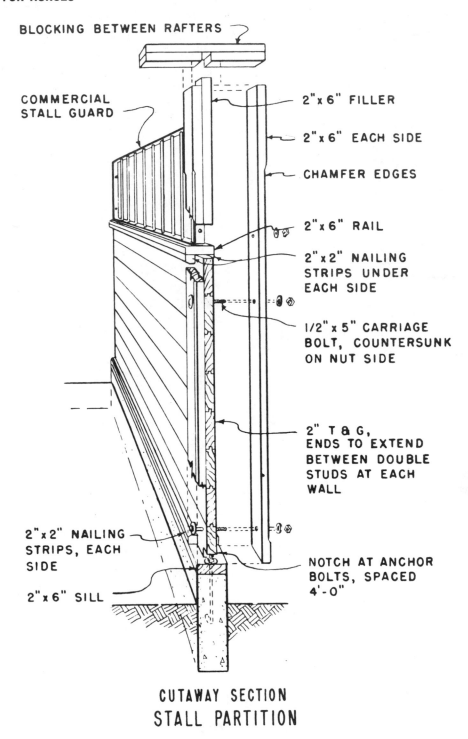

BLOCKING BETWEEN RAFTERS

COMMERCIAL STALL GUARD

2"x 6" FILLER

2"x 6" EACH SIDE

CHAMFER EDGES

2"x 6" RAIL

2"x 2" NAILING STRIPS UNDER EACH SIDE

1/2"x 5" CARRIAGE BOLT, COUNTERSUNK ON NUT SIDE

2" T & G, ENDS TO EXTEND BETWEEN DOUBLE STUDS AT EACH WALL

2"x 2" NAILING STRIPS, EACH SIDE

2"x 6" SILL

NOTCH AT ANCHOR BOLTS, SPACED 4'-0"

CUTAWAY SECTION
STALL PARTITION

Section of partition.

The stall partition shown may be used as part of regular construction in a specially designed horse barn. It also can be used as a partition for a single stall or two in an existing barn renovated to multipurpose use, which includes horse stalls.

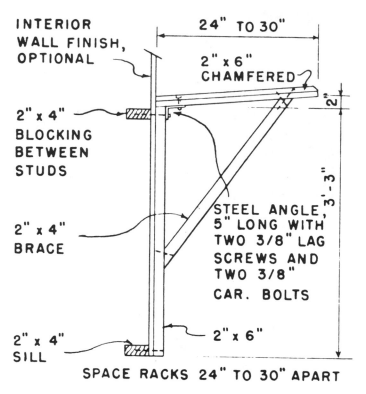

INTERIOR WALL FINISH, OPTIONAL

24" TO 30"

2" x 6" CHAMFERED

2" x 4" BLOCKING BETWEEN STUDS

2" x 4" BRACE

STEEL ANGLE, 5" LONG WITH TWO 3/8" LAG SCREWS AND TWO 3/8" CAR. BOLTS

2"

3'-3"

2" x 4" SILL

2" x 6"

SPACE RACKS 24" TO 30" APART

SADDLE RACK
SCALE: 3/4" = 1'-0"

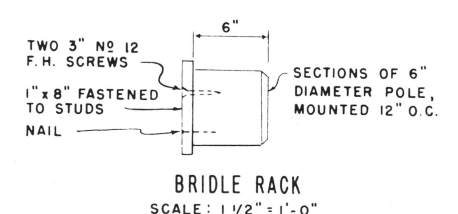

TWO 3" No 12 F.H. SCREWS

1" x 8" FASTENED TO STUDS

NAIL

6"

SECTIONS OF 6" DIAMETER POLE, MOUNTED 12" O.C.

BRIDLE RACK
SCALE: 1 1/2" = 1'-0"

Saddle and bridle racks.

Tack not only will look neater but will last longer if properly stored on racks. Most important, the leather in saddles and bridles will retain its proper shape if stored in correct position.

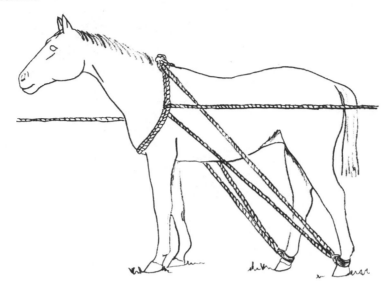

Double side-line casting harness.

This is a practical method of casting and restraining a horse. All that is needed is ample rope (about 60 feet) of ½-inch or larger diameter cord. The collar around the neck is made by tying a bowline on a bight knot. Care must be taken to prevent rope burn. A hopple or a band of leather around the pastern is best to use when available.

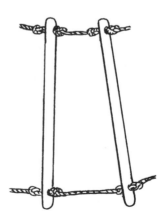

A cradle.

This device keeps a horse from turning or lowering its neck, so it cannot lick a wound on its body. About 18 to 20 pieces of wood with a hole at each end are required. The rope that is threaded through the holes is knotted between each stick. The end of each stick should be sanded smooth so no irritation or cuts result when the animal turns its head.

Ring twitch.

There are many types of twitches that can be improvised as well as purchased. When pressure is applied to the lips of a horse, its attention is diverted so work can be done elsewhere on its body. The ring should be of metal, and 4 or 5 inches in diameter. A light chain or ¼-inch rope is used for the twitch loop.

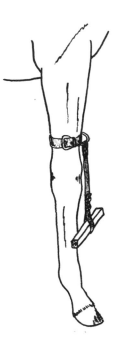

Pawing block.

Horses tend to stop pawing when a light block is attached to the leg, as illustrated. The block should be of hardwood about 1'' x 1'' square and 6 inches long. A leather strap should go around the foreleg. The block should not be left on for long periods, but used only as a temporary restraint.

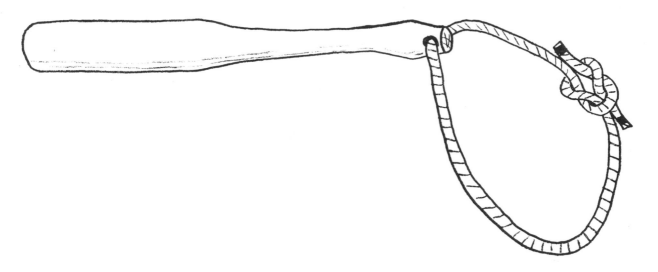

Twitch.

A discarded handle from an axe or hammer makes a quick twitch. Simply drill a hole in the end to allow for the cord, and then thread and tie the loop. Be sure to file and sand the end smooth so there are no splinters.

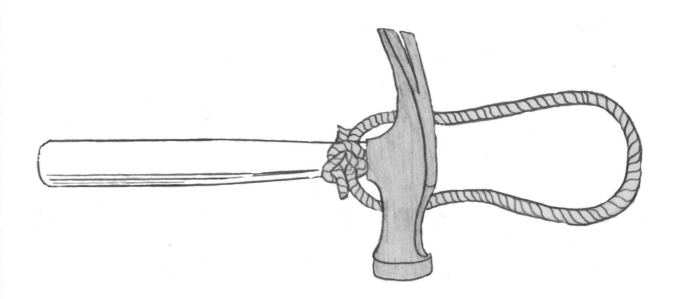

Temporary twitch.

This device is useful when no better twitch is immediately available.

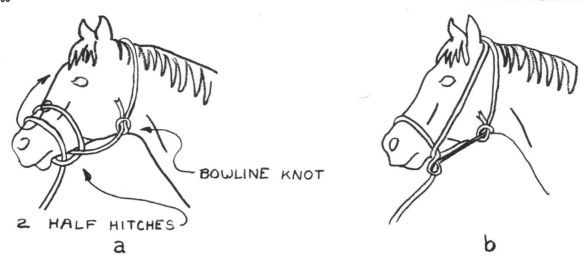

Rope halter.

The illustration is for a quick, temporary, but satisfactory, halter. Tie the rope around the horse's neck with a non-slip knot, then loop as shown in picture (a) and pull tight as shown in picture (b) to complete the halter.

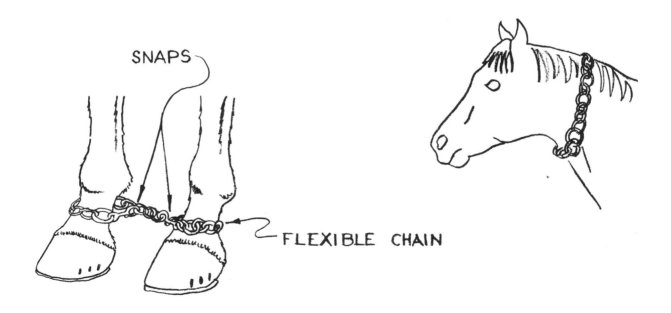

Temporary hobbles.

All that is needed are two snaps and a length of flexible, smooth chain. About 30 inches of chain is ample, depending on the size of the horse. Fasten snaps on each end of the chain so the hobbles will fit the front feet of the horse, as indicated, and cut off any extra links of chain. When not in use the chain can be placed around the horse's neck or in a saddlebag. In order to prevent injury, be certain the animal is used to hobbles before leaving it alone.

Chapter VIII

EQUIPMENT FOR CATTLE

A well-planned cattle layout supported by sturdy equipment will pay big dividends in labor and time saved, increased profits, a reduction in injuries, plus pride in having a smooth-running operation. Whether for dairy cattle, beef cattle, calves, or bulls, there are many items which can be constructed at home or in the shop, easily and inexpensively. Materials found around the farm are cheap and readily available, and can be used to construct most equipment; however, special care should be exercised to see that corners are rounded or ground smooth, or in some cases padded to prevent injury. Poles can be used in place of sawed lumber, but in any case, all wood in contact with the ground should be treated to prevent decay.

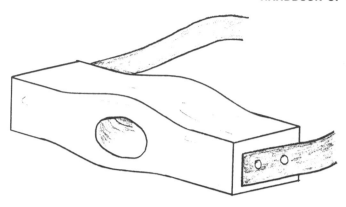

Gag for cattle.

The device is placed in the animal's mouth in order to reduce bloat or insert a tube for medicinal purposes. It is made of hardwood, is 6 or 7 inches wide, and is secured by means of a 1-inch strap that buckles behind the poll of the animal.

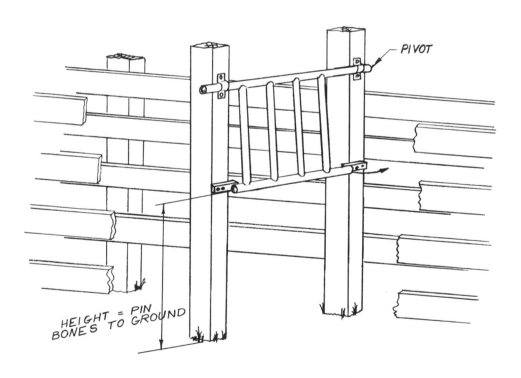

No back gate.

This gate, when installed in chutes or cattle runways, prevents animals from backing up, once they have gone through. It is hinged at the top and the lower bar is high enough off the ground so animals push it up when they go through, but it drops back and prevents their backing up. The lower bar should be just slightly lower than the animals' pin bones in order to firmly stop them, yet encourage their going through. The gate can be counterbalanced if necessary for easy operation. Welded ¾- or 1-inch pipe works well.

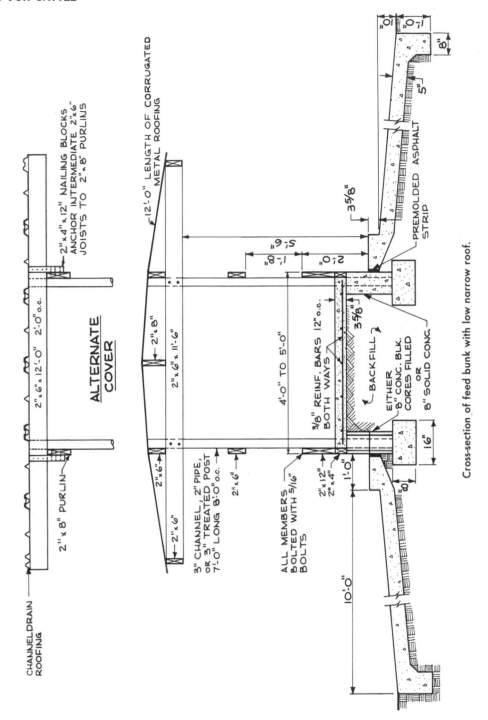

Feed bunk.

One use for a feed bunk is as a molasses feeder. Feed bunks like this one are permanent and can be adapted for conveyor bunks for automatic feeding. (University of Minnesota, Agricultural Extension M-137)

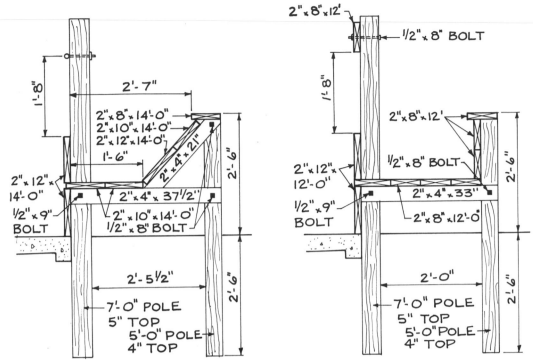

1'-8"

2'-7"

2"x8"x14'-0"
2"x10"x14'-0"
2"x12"x14'-0"
1'-6"
2"x4"x21"

2"x12"x
14'-0"
2"x4"x37½"
½"x9"
BOLT
2"x10"x14'-0"
½"x8" BOLT

2'-6"

2'-5½"

7'-0" POLE
5" TOP
5'-0" POLE
4" TOP

2'-6"

2"x8"x12'

½"x8" BOLT

1'-8"

2"x8"x12'

½"x8" BOLT
2"x12"x
12'-0"
2"x4"x33"
½"x9"
BOLT
2"x8"x12'-0"

2'-6"

2'-0"

7'-0" POLE
5" TOP
5'-0"POLE
4" TOP

2'-6"

Cross-sections of two types of fenceline bunks.

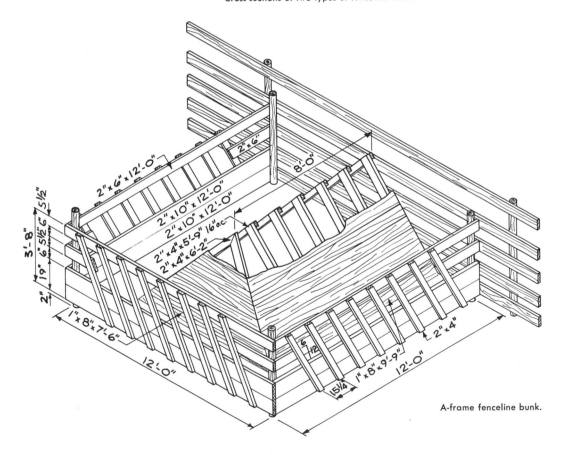

2"x6"

8'-0"

2"x6"x12'-0"
2"x10'x12'-0"
2"x10' x12'-0"
2"x4"x5'-9" 16"o.c.
2"x4"x6'-2"

5½
6
6½
19"
2"
3'-8"

1"x8"x7'-6"

12'-0"

2"x4"

6
12

15¼
1"x8"x9'-9"
12'-0"

A-frame fenceline bunk.

Fenceline bunks.

Fenceline bunks can be of various shapes and may be constructed of wood or concrete. Shown here are two different cross sections of fenceline bunks made from wood. The filling side on one is perpendicular; on the other it slopes outward. If the top rail along the filling side extends inward with an overhang of a couple of inches, there will be less silage pushed overboard by the cattle.

The throat height is 24 inches, the filling side is 30 inches. The rail above the bunk to restrain the cattle can be either a 2 x 8 or a 3/8-inch cable.

The space allowed per head along the bunk depends on whether the animals are on full or limited feed.

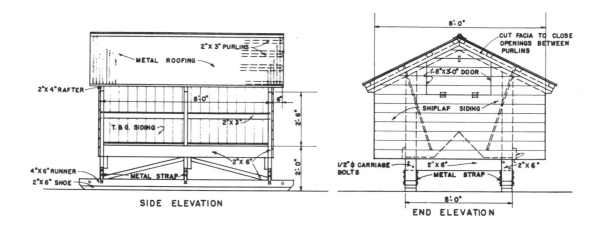

SIDE ELEVATION

END ELEVATION

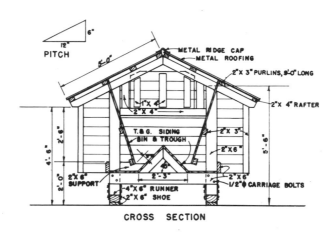

CROSS SECTION

Movable calf creep feeder. (Continued on next page.)

(Oregon State University, Cooperative Extension Work)

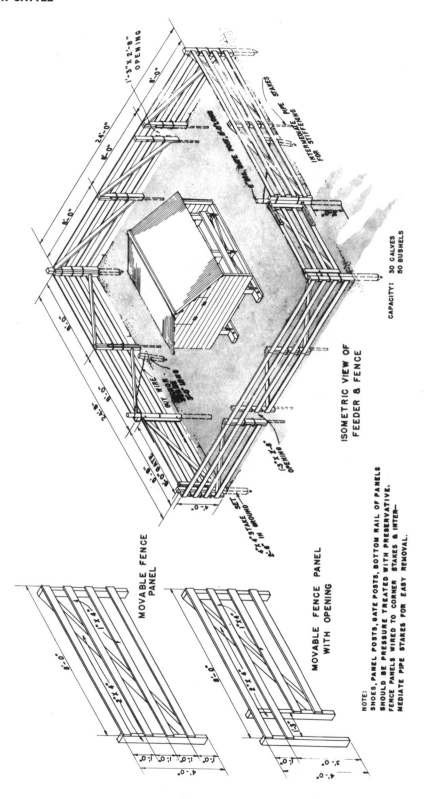

Movable calf creep feeder (continued).

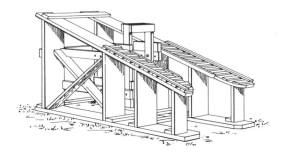

PERSPECTIVE

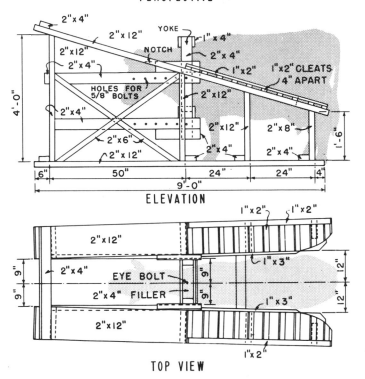

ELEVATION

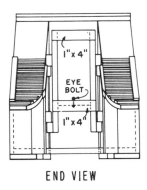

END VIEW

NOTE:
   THE YOKE MAY BE MOVED FORWARD
OR BACK TO SUIT SIZE OF ANIMAL.

ALL WOOD SHOULD BE TREATED WITH
PRESERVATIVE.

TOP VIEW

Cattle-breeding rack.

LIST OF MATERIALS

2—2''x12''x10'-0'' bases
2—2''x12''x10'-0'' uprights
1—2''x 8''x 6'-0'' upright
1—2''x 4''x12'-0'' bottom tie
2—2''x 6''x10'-0'' diagonal braces
2—2''x 4''x12'-0'' extension bars
2—2''x12''x10'-0'' foot rests
1—2''x 4''x 8'-0'' end tie
1—2''x 4''x10'-0'' yoke
1—1''x 4''x 6'-0'' yoke
1—1''x 3''x 8'-0'' foot guard
30—lin. ft. 1''x 2'' cleats
6—lbs. 20d nails
2—lbs. 10d nails
1—¾'' eye bolt 4'' long 1½'' eye

(USDA Miscellaneous Publication 754)

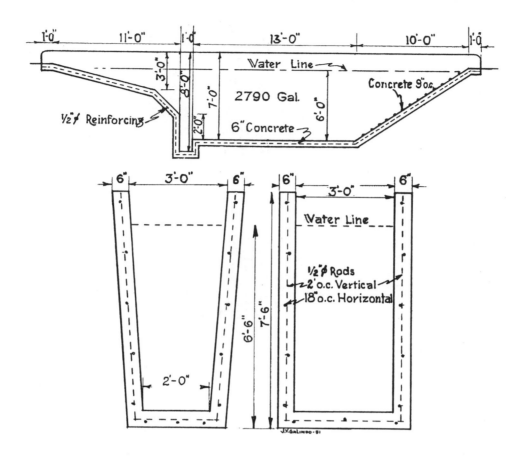

Dipping vat.

On some cattle ranches dipping vats may be needed to control external parasites, especially lice and ticks. The plan shown features a wade-in, which conserves dipping material and makes it easier to drive cattle into the dip. If the wade-in is eliminated, a 30-foot vat is large enough for most ranches, although it can be made larger if necessary. The plan shows longitudinal and alternate cross sections of a concrete dipping vat. The sloping-side type (left) will save a little liquid.

The concrete mixture recommended is 1 sack of cement to 2¼ cubic feet of sand and 3 cubic feet of gravel. To insure waterproof concrete, use a minimum amount of water—not more than 5 gallons per sack of cement for this mix, if the sand is moist. (For more detailed information on waterproof concrete to be used in construction, write the Portland Cement Information Bureau, 564 Market St., San Francisco.)

A waterproofing paint may also be applied to the vat after it has been constructed. One-half-inch steel rods placed 18 inches on centers horizontally and 24 inches vertically are recommended for reinforcing the concrete. Approximately 10 cubic yard of ready-mix concrete will be needed or, if the mixing is done on the job, 60 sacks of cement, 7 cubic yard of sand, and 8 cubic yard of gravel. (University of California, Davis Agricultural Extension Service)

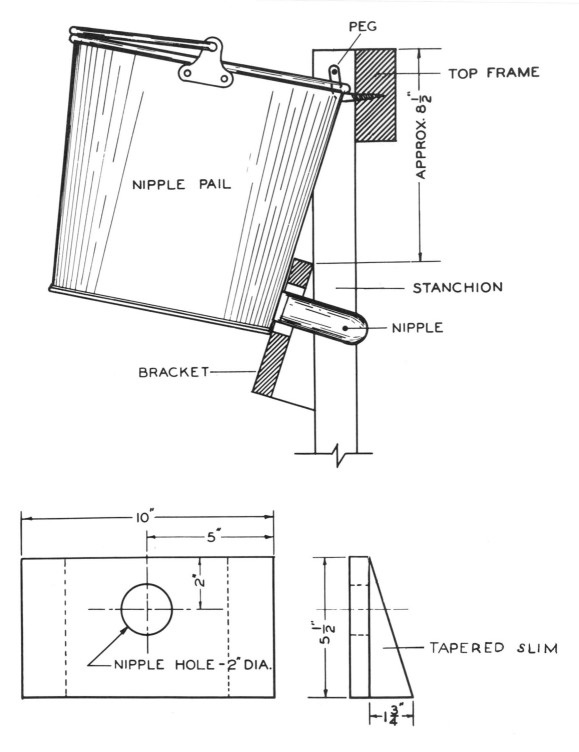

Nipple guard assembly.

The nipple can be purchased at a farm supply house.

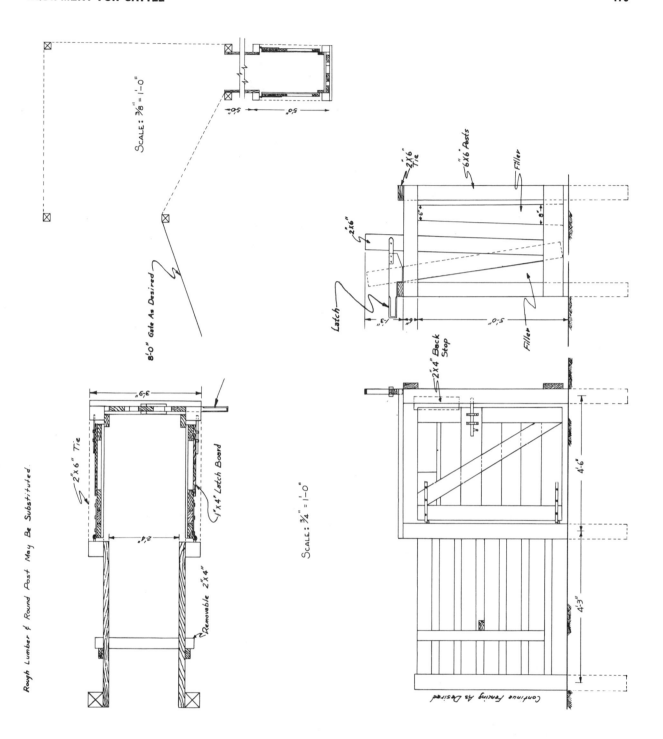

Dairy chute and head gate.

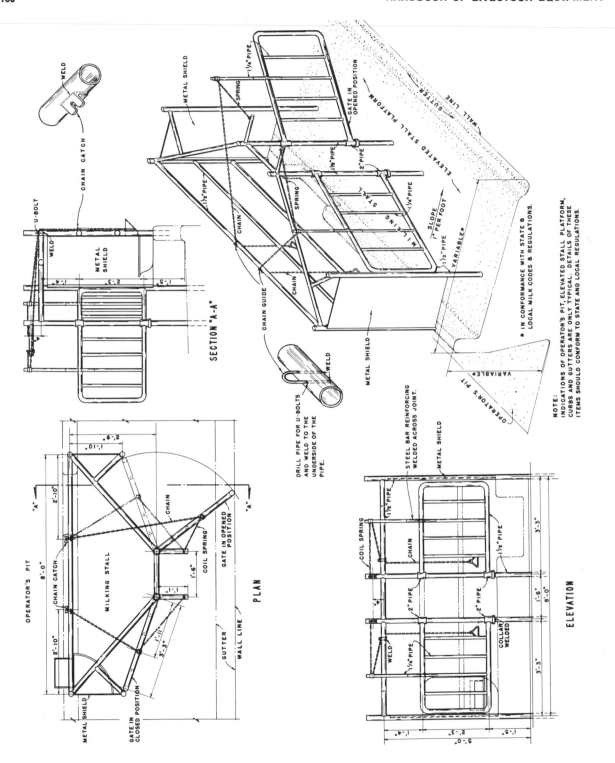

Homemade milking stall.

(Texas A & M University, Cooperative Extension Work in Agriculture)

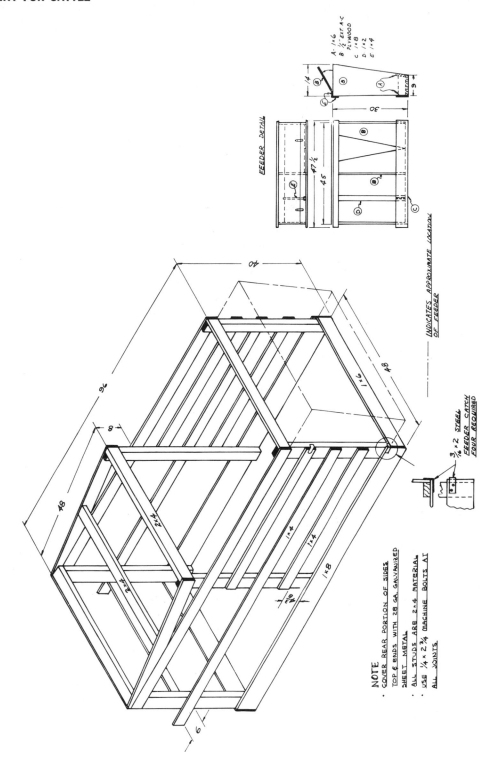

Calf pen.

(California State Polytechnic College, San Luis Obispo)

A Heavy Built-up Shade with Corrugated Roofing

Note: All framing is double: one member each side of pole.

Cattle shade.

Shades to provide cattle relief from intense summer sun will help maintain rate of gain and milk production. When air temperature is in excess of 85° F. (or sometimes even when it is lower) the animals begin to have a higher than normal body temperature. Their appetite and feed intake decline to reduce their metabolic rate and keep them cooler. A shade structure will reduce the radiation heat load on cattle about 50 per cent.

Shades should be 16 to 20 feet wide and can be almost any length in multiples of the support center distance. Shade structures 100 feet or more in length are common. Two or more shades may be desirable in large lots. One shade can serve two pens if it straddles or crosses the dividing fenceline; but opposite sides of each pen must have a similar structure so that all pens receive the same total shaded area. (Continued on next page.)

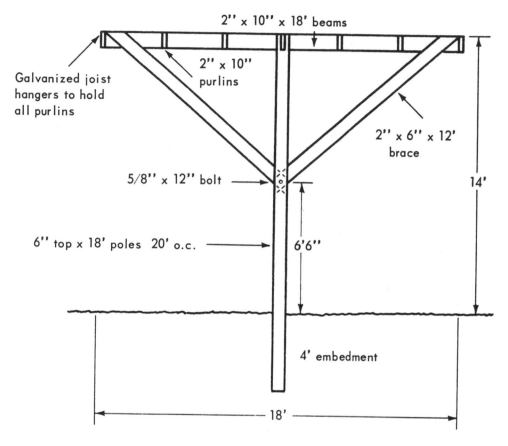

All-Timber Support for Snow Fence or Straw

2'' x 10'' x 18' beams

2'' x 10'' purlins

Galvanized joist hangers to hold all purlins

2'' x 6'' x 12' brace

5/8'' x 12'' bolt

14'

6'' top x 18' poles 20' o.c.

6'6''

4' embedment

18'

Cattle shade (continued).

A single row of support poles is usually favored over a double-pole system because of simplified corral cleanout and reduced likelihood of interference. Double poles may be used in fencelines to reduce sway.

Provide 40 to 60 square feet of shade for each animal. Run shades north-south so that the sun strikes all of the corral at some time each day. This is important in order to prevent wet spots, control fly breeding, and allow the purifying action of the sun's rays. Shades may be run east-west in the hot deserts of the Southwest to take fullest advantage of the cooler north sky. (University of California, Agricultural Extension Service Publication AXT-183)

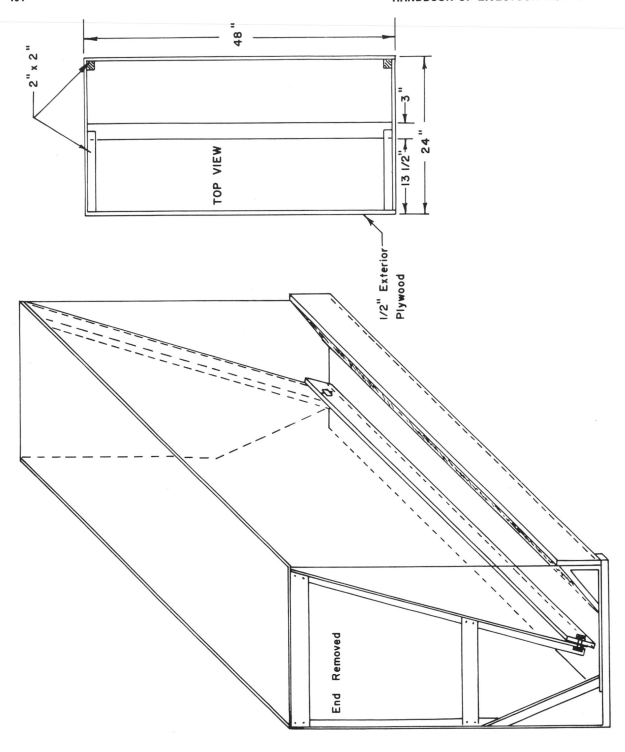

Calf self-feeder.

This feeder is very simple to construct, using exterior glue plywood. Metal straps around the corners should be used to maintain rigidity and make it long-lasting.

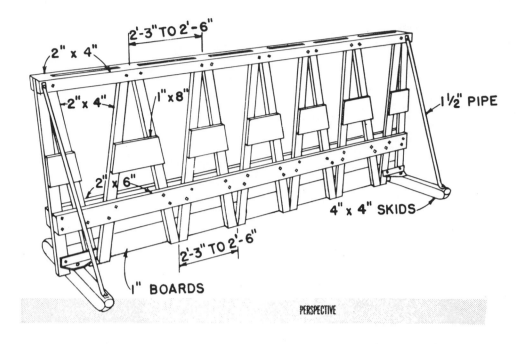

2'-3" TO 2'-6"

2" x 4"

2" x 4"

1" x 8"

1 1/2" PIPE

2" x 6"

4" x 4" SKIDS

2'-3" TO 2'-6"

1" BOARDS

PERSPECTIVE

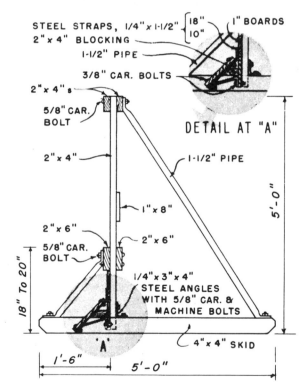

STEEL STRAPS, 1/4" x 1-1/2" { 18" 10" } 1" BOARDS

2" x 4" BLOCKING

1-1/2" PIPE

3/8" CAR. BOLTS

DETAIL AT "A"

2" x 4"s

5/8" CAR. BOLT

1-1/2" PIPE

2" x 4"

1" x 8"

2" x 6"

5/8" CAR. BOLT

2" x 6"

1/4" x 3" x 4" STEEL ANGLES WITH 5/8" CAR. & MACHINE BOLTS

5'-0"

18" TO 20"

'A'

4" x 4" SKID

1'-6"

5'-0"

Self-feeding fence.

This type of fence is generally used to self-feed silage or chopped hay in a pit or fence silo.

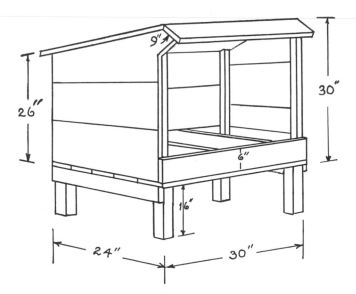

Weatherproof mineral box.

All livestock should have access to minerals, especially common salt and other minerals, depending on area deficiencies.

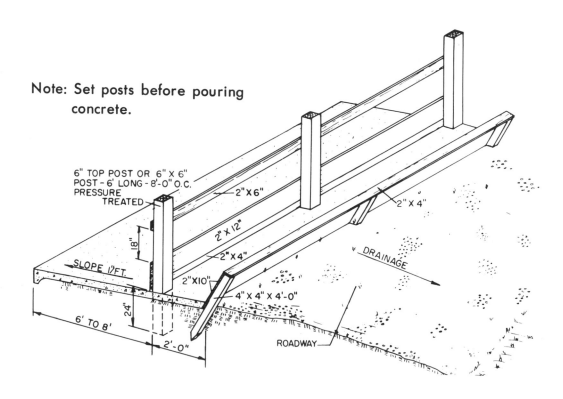

Fenceline bunk.

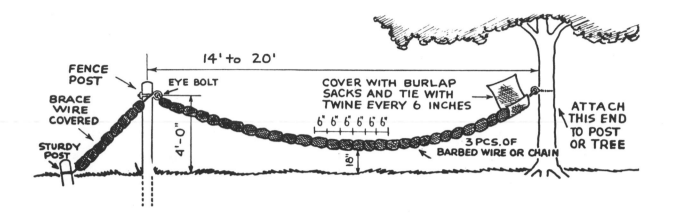

Cable backrubbers.

Backrubbers are used primarily for control of external parasites, especially hornflies, etc., on cattle.

MATERIALS NEEDED

2 eye bolts or heavy wire for securing to post
2 eye rings or snaps
14 to 20 burlap sacks
40 to 50 20-inch pieces of binding twine or cord
3 20- to 25-foot pieces of barbed wire, cable, or chain
Heavy fence and brace posts
Heavy wire for bracing

Place two posts 14 to 20 feet apart. Posts should be 6 inches in diameter, 8 feet long, and be of either treated wood or wood which is naturally durable. Insert at least 3 feet in the ground and allow 4½ feet to remain aboveground. In many locations trees can be located which will serve as posts. Brace the posts as illustrated in the diagram.

Stretch a cable, chain, or several strands of barbed wire between the posts and allow to sag in the center to within about 18 inches of the ground. Wrap the burlap on the cable as illustrated.

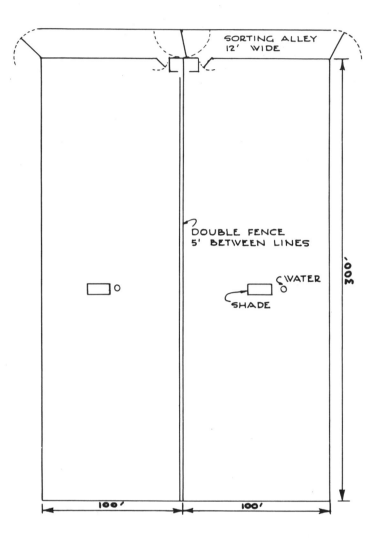

Herd bull paddocks and sun shades.

This general plan of herd bull paddocks, barns, and sorting alley will serve as a guide. If native grass pasture is used the lots will need to be at least twice as large or the grass will become overgrazed.

In the warmer climates the water tank placed on the east side of the sun shade will help in keeping the water cooler during the summer months.

One end, or at least a portion, of the lane shown in the drawing should be gravelled so that there will be a place to breed cows in wet weather where the bull will not injure himself by slipping in the mud. If only a portion is gravelled, another gate should enclose the section. (Continued on next page.)

CORRUGATED ROOFING

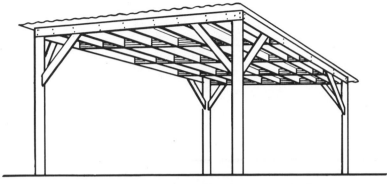

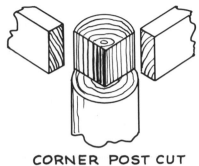

CORNER POST CUT
TO TAKE 2X6s

Sun shade — 12 ft. x 12 ft.

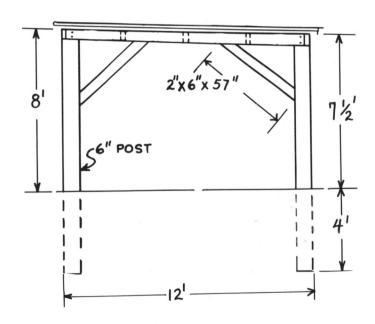

8'

2"x6"x 57"

6" POST

7½'

4'

12'

Herd bull paddocks and sun shades (continued).

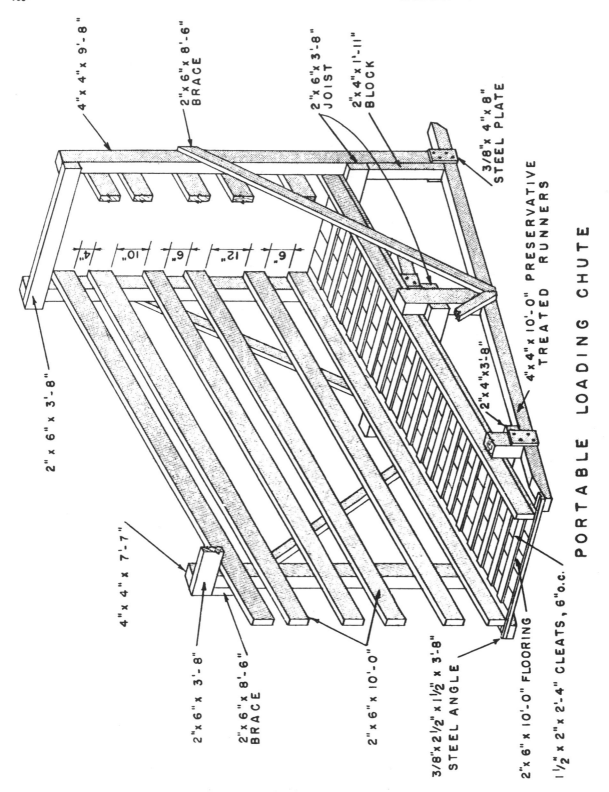

Portable loading chute.

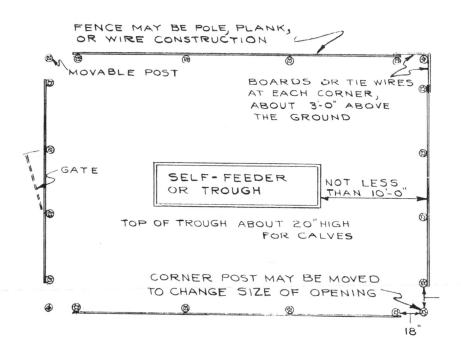

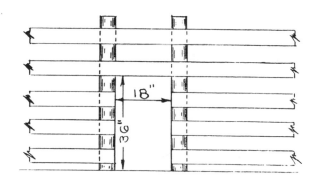

Creep feeder.

There are times when it becomes necessary or profitable to creep feed calves. Calves will begin to take a little grain at two weeks of age. A self-feeder 10 feet long will take care of 40 to 50 calves. Not all creep feeders need protection from the weather.

BILL OF MATERIALS

Quantity	Description
8	2x6—12 ft. rafters
3	2x6—12 ft. rafter ties
4	2x6—10 ft. corner braces
4	treated posts 6 in. top—12 ft. posts
10	sheets corrugated iron roofing—7 ft. roof

(American Hereford Association)

Chapter IX

EQUIPMENT FOR SHEEP

In order for the sheep enterprise to be most successful and profitable, buildings and equipment must provide for labor efficiency and a suitable environment. The flock's contribution to the total farm income should be able to justify the time and energy and the money invested.

University of Missouri Bulletin 655 emphasizes that sheepmen should plan for efficiency. Generally speaking, about 40 ewes is the minimum-size flock for a profitable operation.

Most sheepmen agree that winter cold is less damaging than summer heat, providing sheep can be kept dry. Lambing is the most critical period, so dry stalls, non-draft quarters, heat lamps, etc., are excellent items if lambing takes place during inclement weather.

The shelter and care requirements change from one season to another, making movable equipment desirable. Gates, feeders, and other equipment should be stored conveniently in the same building, and an all-weather watering system should be provided.

Sheep barns should provide 12 to 15 square feet of floor space for each grown animal. Ten to 12 linear inches of grain troughs and hay mangers should be furnished for each animal. Where a combination hay and grain feeder is used, some floor space can be saved. Feed mangers should be made in convenient lengths for moving and for arrangement. An arrangement where the feed mangers fit between the interior posts or poles of the shelter is suggested. One or two feed mangers may be shortened to provide a small passageway for transferring animals.

The sheep barn should be located on a well-drained site and faced to take advantage of the southwesterly summer breezes and still provide protection from the northwest winter winds. A shelter opening to the east can be located to fulfill these requirements. Dogproof fences around the night yard are essential in many localities. They are an added investment but return much in safety and good neighbor relations.

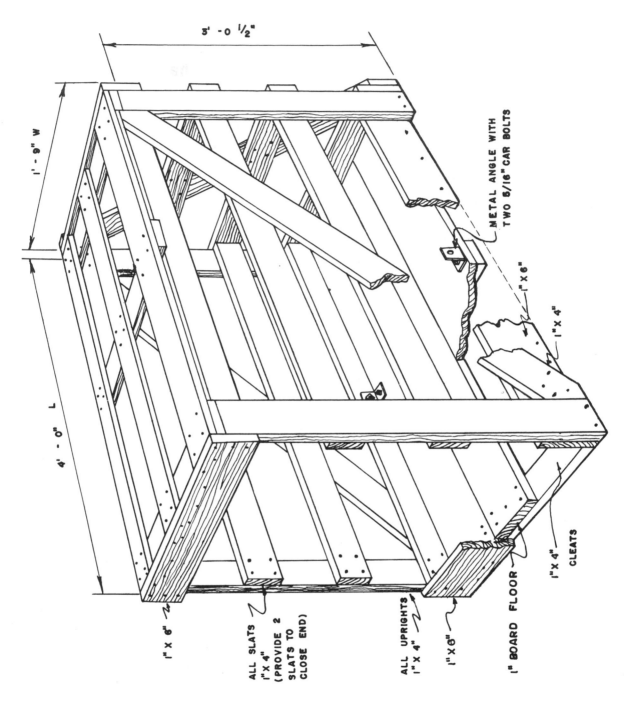

Shipping crate.

Shipping crates are handy items on any ranch. Often times they are more acceptable than pickup racks. These crates can easily be used to transport single animals in the back of a station-wagon or pickup and then slid out on the ground to store in the shade, leaving the vehicle free for other use. Swine or calves also will fit this type crate. Sliding or hinged ends make it even more versatile.

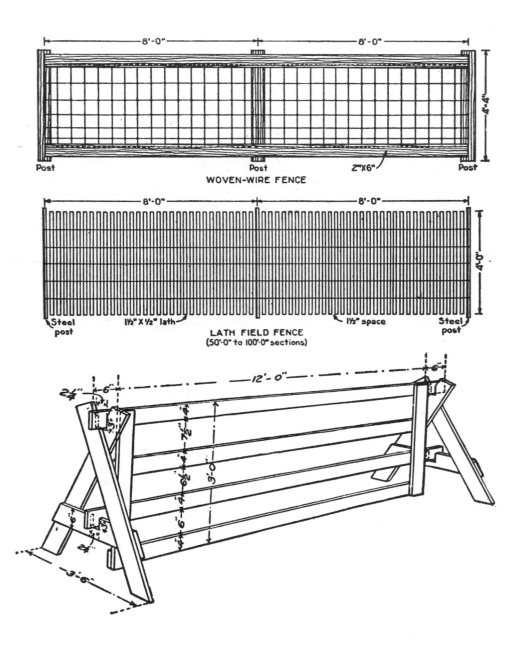

Three economical types of sheep fences.

Upper, combination wire and boards; middle, a movable slat or snow fence; lower, a portable fence useful for pasture and soiling crops and temporary lots. (USDA Farmers' Bulletin 1832)

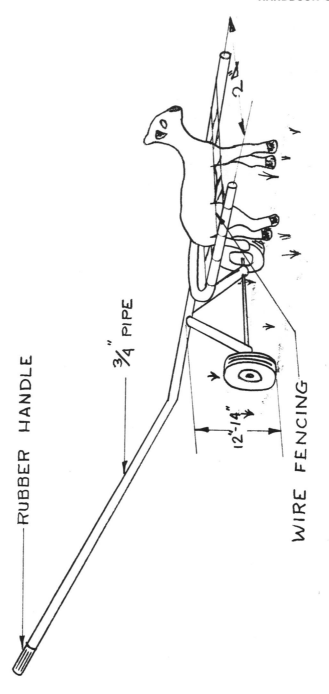

Lamb cart.

This is an extremely handy and effective piece of equipment in moving newborn lambs. If the weak, newborn lamb is placed on the wire netting with its feet dangling off the ground, it can be easily pulled to a place of shelter and the ewe will follow. The ewe follows because she can stay close to the lamb without getting close to the shepherd. An old toy tricycle gear with wheels adapts easily to the construction of the cart.

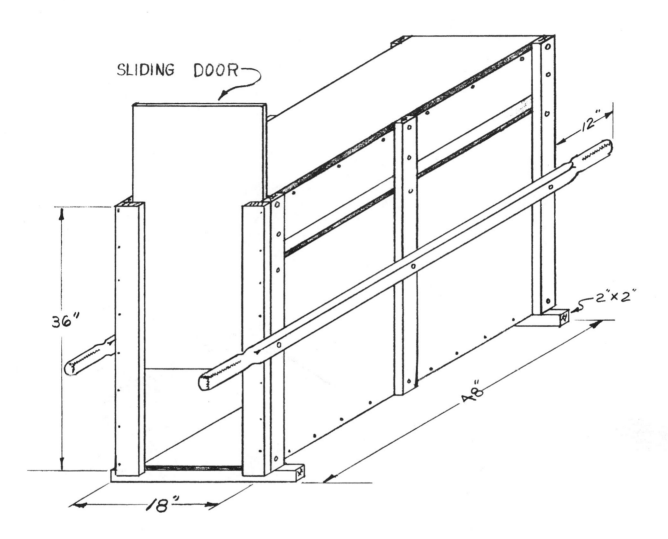

SLIDING DOOR

36″

18″

12″

2″×2″

48″

Shipping or carrying crate.

The entire crate can be made of ½-inch plywood and light wooden strips. Sheep, calves, and swine are easily and quietly carried because they cannot see out.

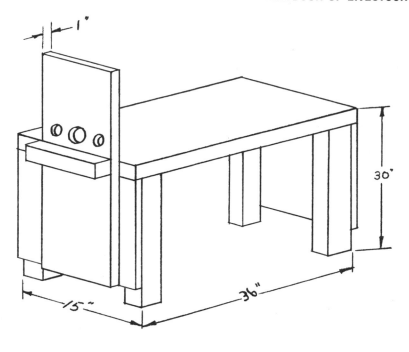

Sheep-docking table.

This table makes it easy to hold lambs and at the same time protects the lamb from injury when docking with a heated iron. Light pine construction of 1-inch boards and 2 x 2 legs is ample.

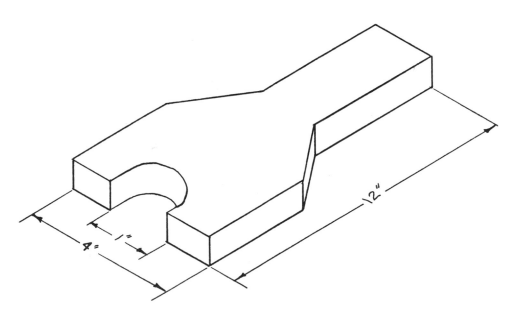

Docking board.

This device can easily be made from a piece of smooth 1-inch board. If placed over the tail it protects the lamb when a heated iron is used and makes the job easier to do.

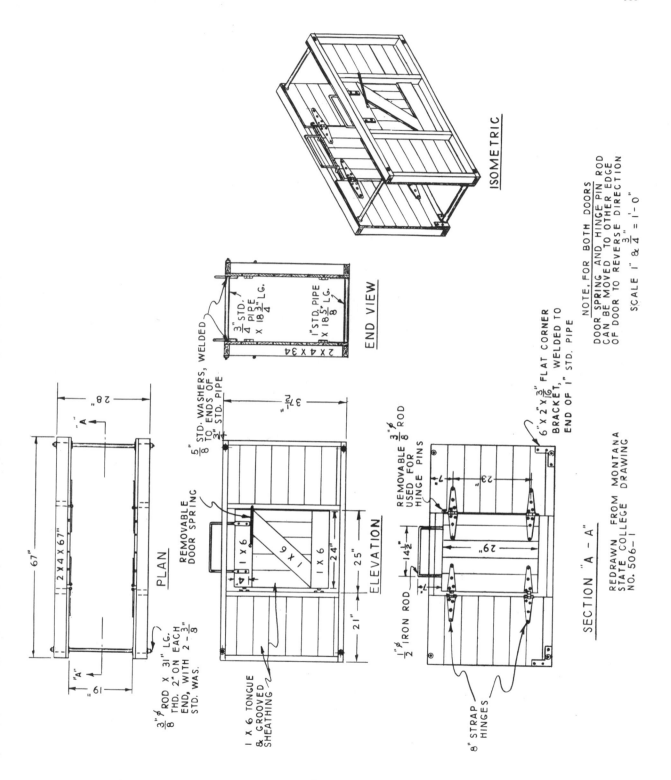

ISOMETRIC

END VIEW

$\frac{3}{4}$" STD. PIPE X 18 $\frac{3}{4}$" LG.

1" STD. PIPE X 18 $\frac{5}{8}$" LG.

2 X 4 X 34

$\frac{5}{8}$" STD. WASHERS, WELDED TO ENDS OF $\frac{3}{4}$" STD. PIPE

NOTE, FOR BOTH DOORS
DOOR SPRING AND HINGE PIN ROD
CAN BE MOVED TO OTHER EDGE
OF DOOR TO REVERSE DIRECTION

SCALE 1" & $\frac{3}{4}$" = 1'-0"

PLAN

28"

2 X 4 X 67"

67"

61"

"A"

"A"

$\frac{3}{8}$"⌀ ROD X 31" LG.
THD. 2" ON EACH
END, WITH 2-$\frac{3}{8}$"
STD. WAS.

REMOVABLE
DOOR SPRING

ELEVATION

37 $\frac{1}{2}$"

1 X 6

1 X 6

1 X 6

24"

25"

21"

1 X 6 TONGUE
& GROOVED
SHEATHING

SECTION "A - A"

REMOVABLE $\frac{3}{8}$"⌀ ROD
USED FOR HINGE PINS

$\frac{1}{2}$"⌀ IRON ROD

14 $\frac{1}{2}$"

7"

7"

23"

29"

6" X 2" X $\frac{3}{16}$" FLAT CORNER
BRACKET, WELDED TO
END OF 1" STD. PIPE

8" STRAP
HINGES

REDRAWN FROM MONTANA
STATE COLLEGE DRAWING
NO. 506-1

Three-way cutting gate.

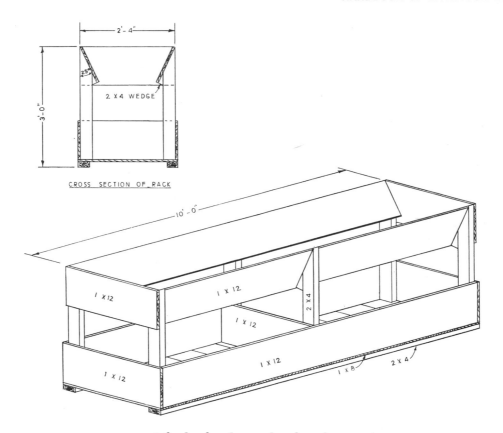

A feeder for chopped or long hay.

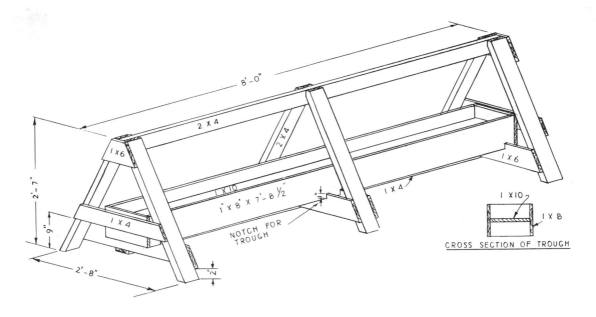

Reversible portable grain trough.

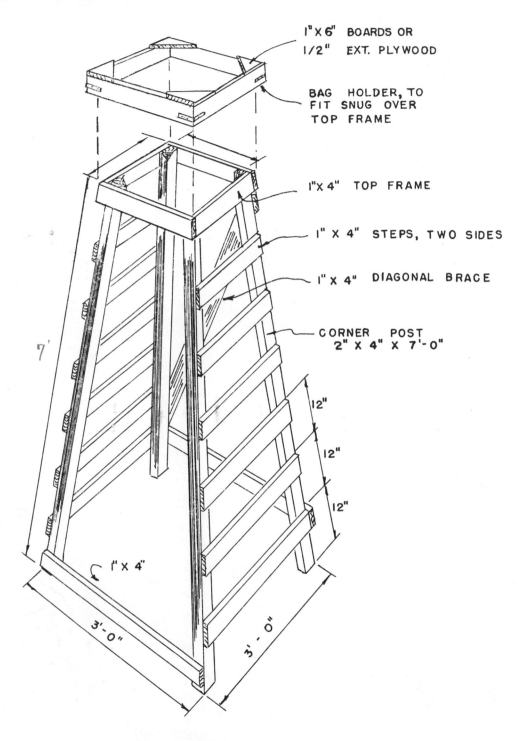

1" X 6" BOARDS OR
1/2" EXT. PLYWOOD

BAG HOLDER, TO
FIT SNUG OVER
TOP FRAME

1" X 4" TOP FRAME

1" X 4" STEPS, TWO SIDES

1" X 4" DIAGONAL BRACE

CORNER POST
2" X 4" X 7'-0"

12"

12"

12"

7'

1" X 4"

3'-0"

3'-0"

Wool-packing rack.

A 4 x 4 platform or collar made of ½-inch plywood can be built around the top of the rack if desired. This allows the sacker a place to stand or store wool while filling the wool sack. Either rough or smooth lumber can be used.

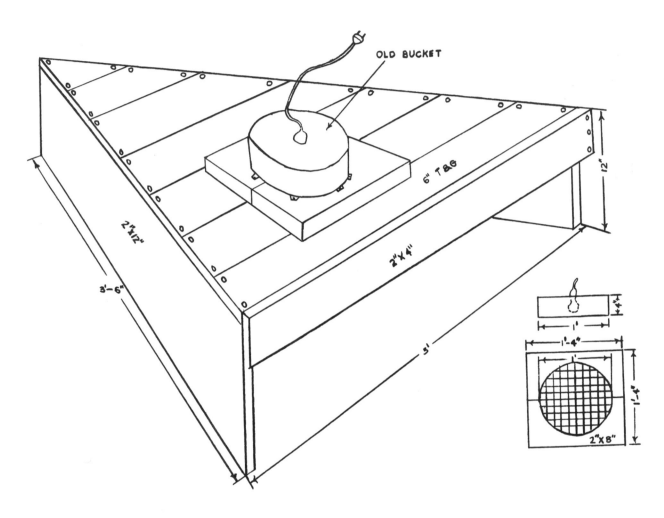

Lamb brooder.

This brooder can also be used for newborn pigs. If desired, the entire brooder can be built of plywood.

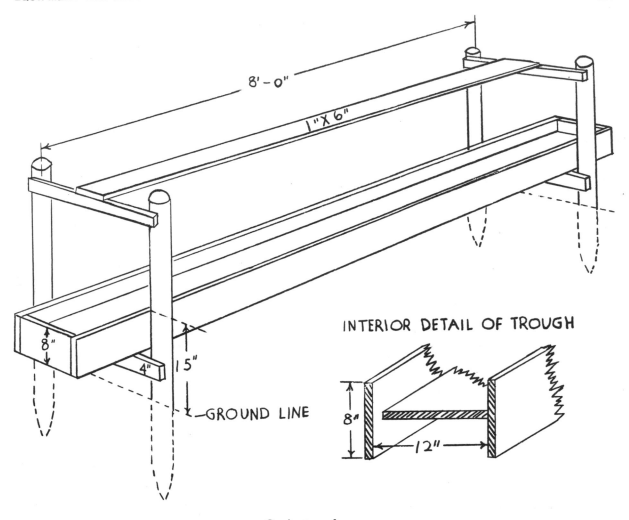

INTERIOR DETAIL OF TROUGH

Grain trough.

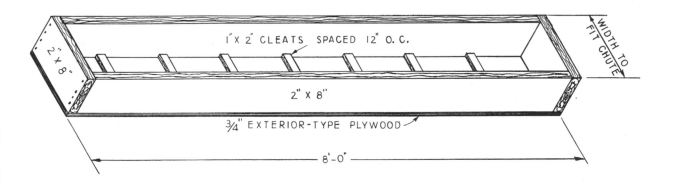

Portable footbath.

The footbath can be placed inside the loading chute for easy use when treating foot problems.

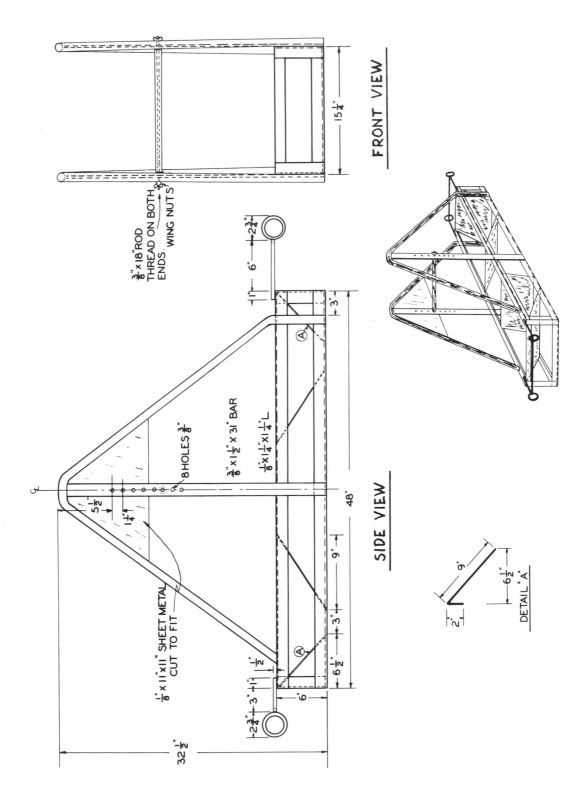

FRONT VIEW

15 1/4"

3/8" x 18" ROD THREAD ON BOTH ENDS. WING NUTS

SIDE VIEW

8 HOLES 3/8"

5 1/2"

1 1/4"

3/8" x 1 1/2" x 31" BAR

1/8" x 1 1/4" x 1 1/4" L

48"

9"

3"

6 1/2"

1/8" x 11" x 11" SHEET METAL CUT TO FIT

1/2"

3"

6"

2 3/4"   3"   1"

32 1/2"

6"   2 3/4"

3"

DETAIL 'A'

9"

6 1/2"

2"

Hoof-trimming cradle.

Two widths are built into the cradle for different-size sheep. To use this cradle:

1. Place one hand on tail and one hand under neck of sheep.
2. Back sheep into cradle and push down on tail and lift under neck to trip rear legs. Sheep will settle into built-in saddle and then can be tilted back against crossbar.
3. The back rest or crossbar height is important and should be adjusted to be at junction of shoulder and neck.

   Treat feet as needed.

4. Release sheep; lift opposite end of cradle to tilt animal to fall forward.

To handle small sheep, a cradle having less width can be used; or sides can be filled with plywood panels to provide the desired width.

```
4 pc. angle iron      ⅛" x  1¼" x  5¾"
4 pc. angle iron      ⅛" x  1¼" x 48"
2 pc. angle iron      ⅛" x  1¼" x 15"
2 pc. sheet metal     ⅛" x 11  " x 12¾"
2 pc. sheet metal     ⅛" x 10½" x 12¾"
2 pc. bar             ⅜" x  1½" x 31"
2 pc. pipe            1" x 78  "
1 pc. pipe            1" x 14¾"
2 pc. rod             ½" x  7  "
2 pc. rod             ½" x  4  "
2 pc. rod             ½" x 14  "
4 pc. rod rings       ½" x  2¾" dia. o.d.
1 pc. rod ⅜" x 18" thread on both ends.
2 pc. sheet metal ⅛" x 16" x 19" cut to fit. (optional)
```

(Oregon State University)

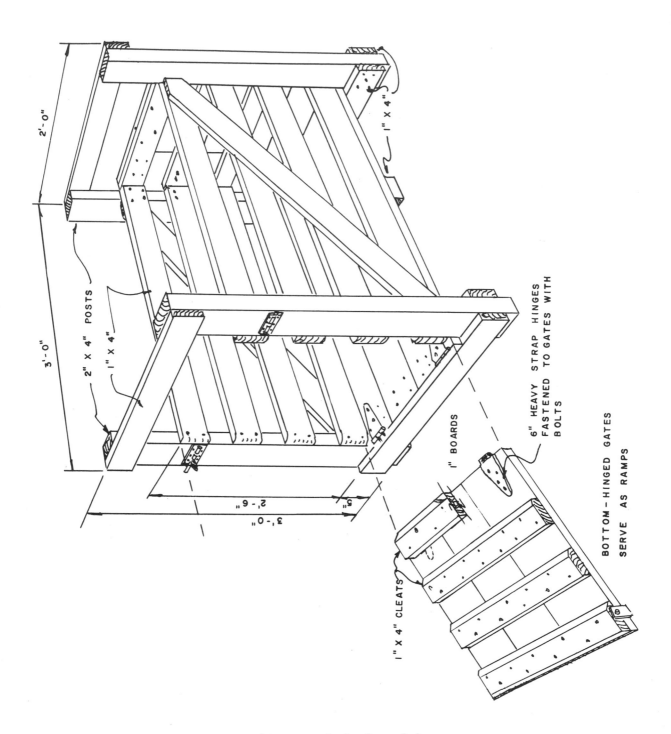

Weighing crate for lambs and sheep.

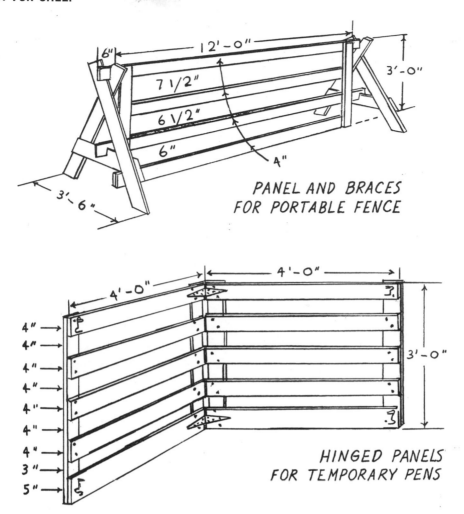

PANEL AND BRACES
FOR PORTABLE FENCE

HINGED PANELS
FOR TEMPORARY PENS

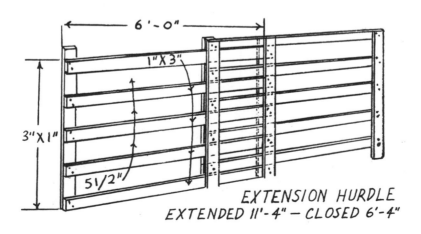

EXTENSION HURDLE
EXTENDED 11'-4" — CLOSED 6'-4"

Panels or racks used for temporary fences.

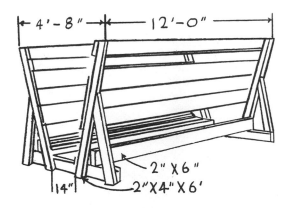

Self-feeder hayrack.

(Agricultural Engineering Extension, Montana State University)

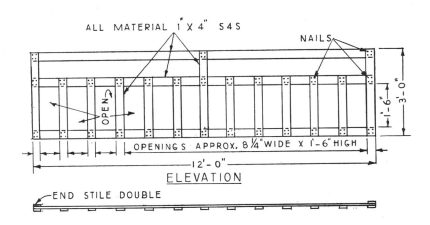

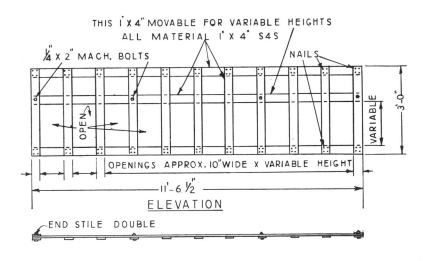

Creep panels.

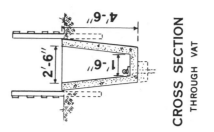

CROSS SECTION
THROUGH VAT

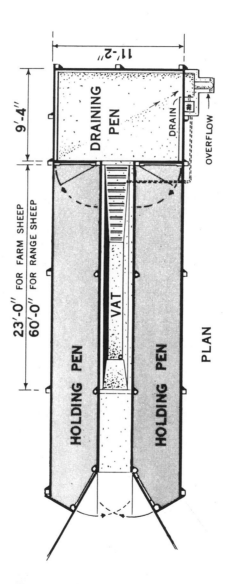

PLAN

Dipping vat.

Drawings show construction details for a concrete vat and draining and holding pens. The vat should be 60 feet long for range sheep, but it need be only 23 feet long for farm sheep. The shorter length may also be used for hogs. (USDA Plan No. 5390)

Chapter X

EQUIPMENT FOR SWINE

Raising swine involves the use of more equipment than most classes of livestock. This is necessary because swine are generally confined more than other animals; therefore, fences, waterers, feeders, etc., all must be provided rather than letting animals live off the land as with cattle and sheep.

Equipment must be well constructed and unusually well braced to combat the rooting habits of animals as strong as swine. The disposal of manure is frequently a problem of animals in confinement, so concrete is often used to brace buildings, and the design is slanted toward easy cleanout. The use of bolts, corner braces, and welded joints is essential if equipment is to last and be economical.

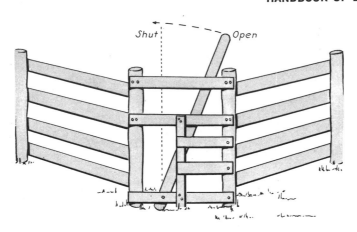

Pig-catching gate.

The swinging lever holds the animal when it locks just behind the animal's jowls. Such a gate can be placed between two pens to ring swine or identify them from notches. Generally, a swinging gate is necessary in order to force animals into the headgate. Strong posts and 2 x 4 lumber will handle most animals. The gate could be constructed, also, of welded pipe 1 inch or larger.

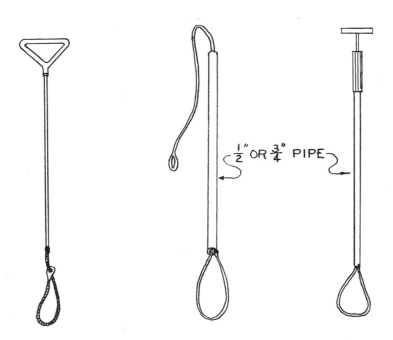

Swine snares.

These three devices are all satisfactory for holding swine for restraining purposes. Each device works on a slightly different principle, but can be made from materials commonly found around the ranch or shop. Rope will work, but thin, flexible cable is best. Each device should be from 30 inches to 36 inches long.

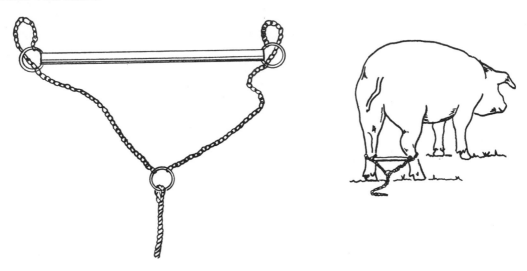

Swine hopples.

This device is made from a piece of 1-inch or 1¼-inch pipe about 16 inches long with a 2-inch ring welded on each end. Two flexible chains about 20 inches to 24 inches long are fastened to each end of the hopple, as indicated, and both joined by a third ring which connects the two chains. To use, hold the animal by the snout, using a snare, and then stretch it out by putting on the hopples and pulling it out until it loses its balance.

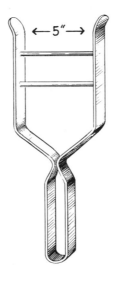

Speculum.

The speculum is used for holding open the jaws of a pig. It is operated by inserting horizontally into the mouth as far back as possible, then pushing down over the chin until in a vertical position. The device can be purchased, or easily made of 1/8'' x 3/4'' flat, mild steel riveting in two 5-inch long 1/4-inch diameter steel rods, as indicated.

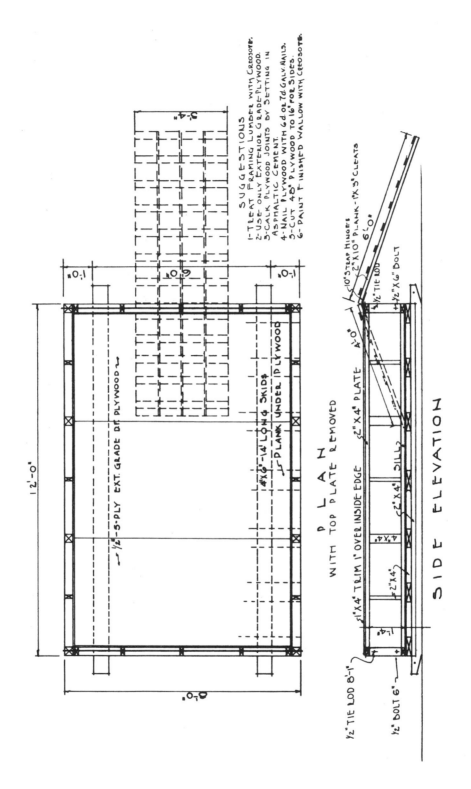

SUGGESTIONS
1—TREAT FRAMING LUMBER WITH CREOSOTE.
2—USE ONLY EXTERIOR GRADE PLYWOOD.
3—CALK PLYWOOD JOINTS BY SETTING IN ASPHALTIC CEMENT.
4—NAIL PLYWOOD WITH 6d or 7d GALV. NAILS.
5—CUT 4'X8" PLYWOOD TO 16" FOR SIDES.
6—PAINT FINISHED WALLOW WITH CREOSOTE.

PLAN
WITH TOP PLATE REMOVED

SIDE ELEVATION

Portable hog wallow.

According to University of Wisconsin Extension Service Circular 43, it will pay you to invest in a hog wallow: if you have 30 or more hogs, if you have running water, if the natural shade you have is poor, if your hogs need treatment for lice and mites (mange), or if you plan to sell your pig crop early and have to "finish" off during hot weather.

A hog wallow can be built of just about any kind of material you have available. Here are some points to remember in making one:

1. Don't make it too heavy. It should be easy to move from pasture to pasture.
2. Build it sturdy. It will get hard use, and you will want it to remain watertight for several years.
3. Use materials that are easy to work with.
4. Keep the cost down by choosing inexpensive material.

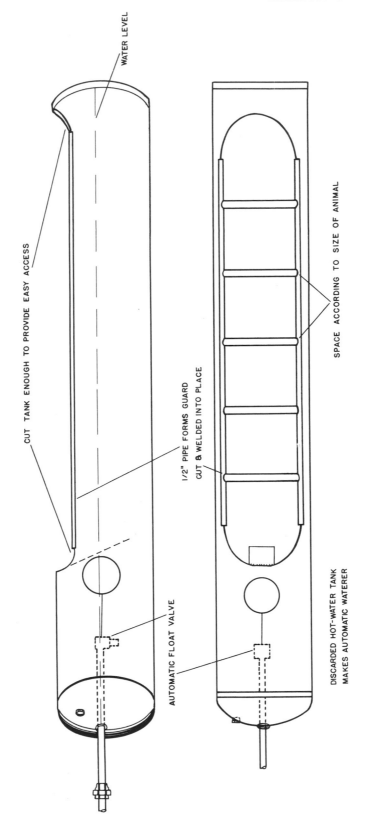

WATER LEVEL

CUT TANK ENOUGH TO PROVIDE EASY ACCESS

1/2" PIPE FORMS GUARD
CUT & WELDED INTO PLACE

SPACE ACCORDING TO SIZE OF ANIMAL

AUTOMATIC FLOAT VALVE

DISCARDED HOT-WATER TANK
MAKES AUTOMATIC WATERER

Automatic hog waterer.

Any tank of proper size and shape will do. A 20- to 40-gallon discarded water tank will do nicely. Construct the grate from ½-inch pipe.

Cutting the tank is accomplished with either a cutting torch or a slitting chisel. Remember, hot galvanized metal gives off poisonous zinc fumes which are dangerous in unventilated areas! Be sure to leave the tab which bends down and guards the float.

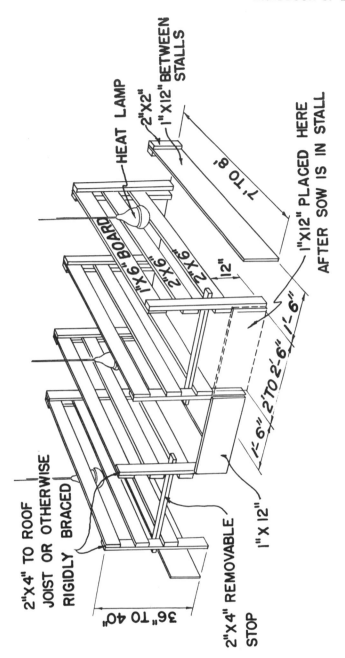

Farrowing stall.

Farrowing stalls are becoming common. These have the advantages of saving space and, more important, protecting the pigs from the sow. With their use, there is a trend toward either multiple-unit houses or permanent central farrowing houses.

Multiple farrowings throughout the year, together with the use of farrowing stalls, are making the central farrowing house much more economical than in the past. Since stalls reduce the floor area needed per sow, houses can be smaller than they used to be. (University of Illinois Extension Service)

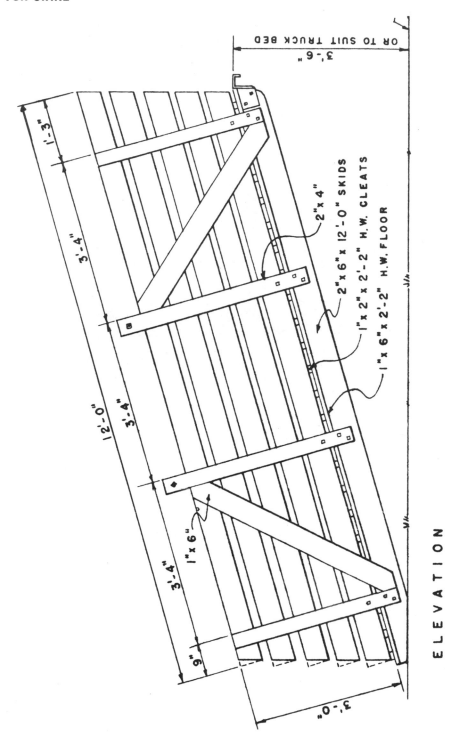

Portable loading chute.

The inside width should be approximately 24 inches, and metal corner braces should be used at stress points. (Texas A & M Extension Service)

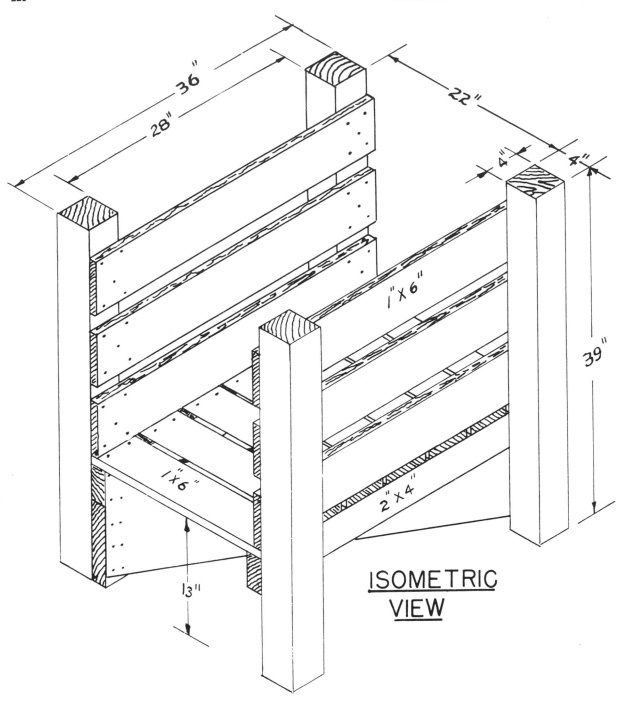

ISOMETRIC
VIEW

Pig separator.

The separator is placed in a runway, and when the sow and little pigs go through, the sow steps over and her young pigs are shunted into another pen by the lower separator partition, as illustrated. (Texas A & M Extension Service)

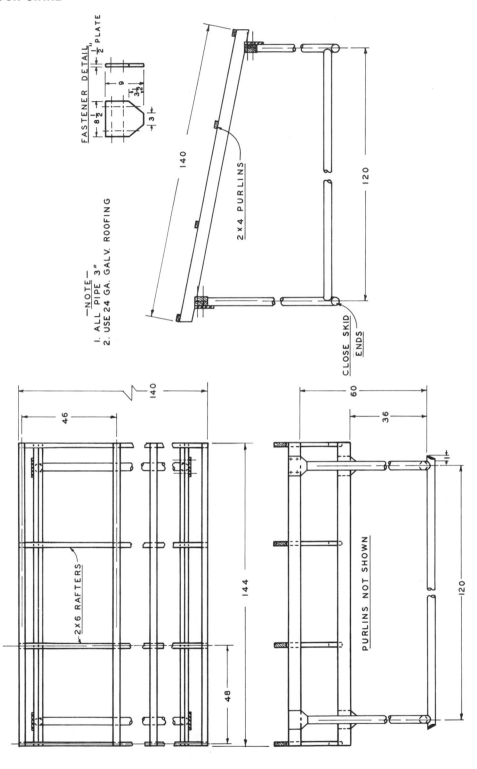

FASTENER DETAIL

½" PLATE

9

3½

2

8½

3

—NOTE—
1. ALL PIPE 3"
2. USE 24 GA. GALV. ROOFING

140

2×4 PURLINS

120

CLOSE SKID ENDS

140

46

2×6 RAFTERS

144

48

60

36

PURLINS NOT SHOWN

120

Portable hog shade.

The roof can be made of plywood 1-inch lumber shingles, or even galvanized sheet metal.

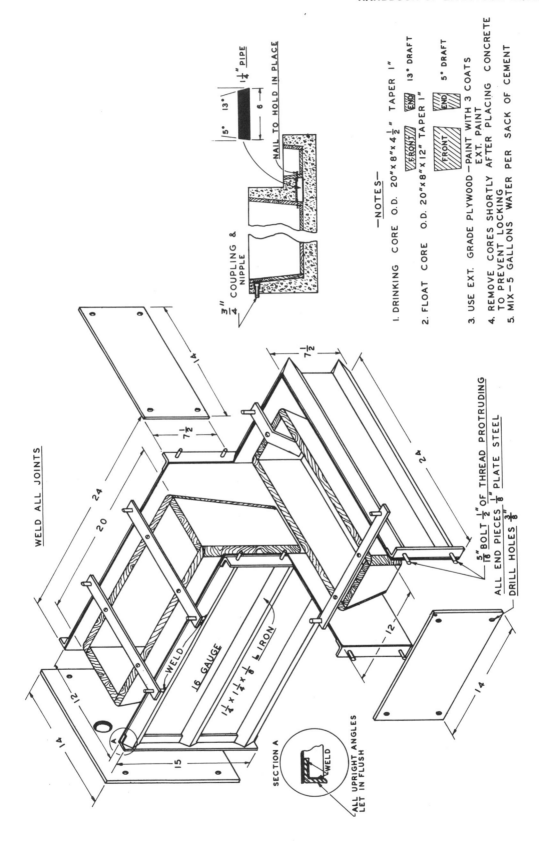

—NOTES—

1. DRINKING CORE O.D. 20"x8"x4½" TAPER 1"

2. FLOAT CORE O.D. 20"x8"x12" TAPER 1"

3. USE EXT. GRADE PLYWOOD—PAINT WITH 3 COATS EXT. PAINT

4. REMOVE CORES SHORTLY AFTER PLACING CONCRETE TO PREVENT LOCKING

5. MIX—5 GALLONS WATER PER SACK OF CEMENT

Hog watering trough.

Once the form is made, many troughs can be made quickly and economically. (California State Polytechnic College, Dept. of Agricultural Engineering)

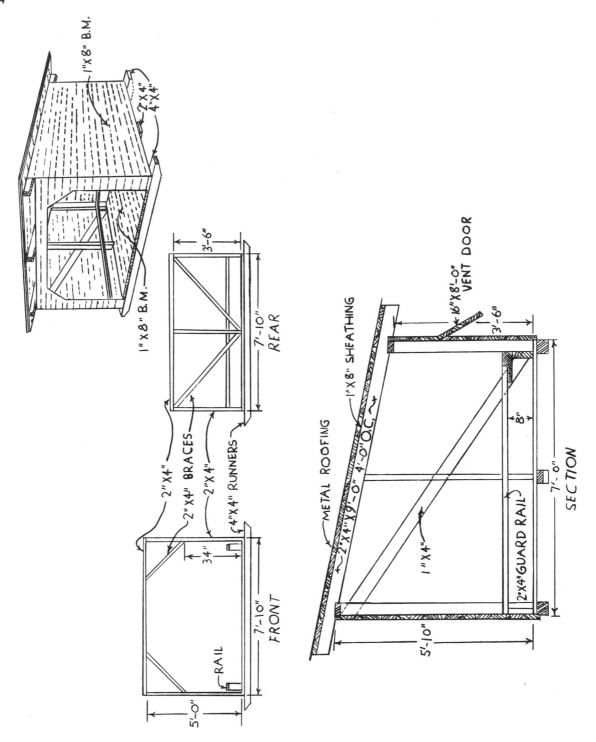

Shed-type hog house.

Note that guard rails are an essential part of this type of hog house. Guard rails may be hinged to facilitate cleaning. (Montana State University)

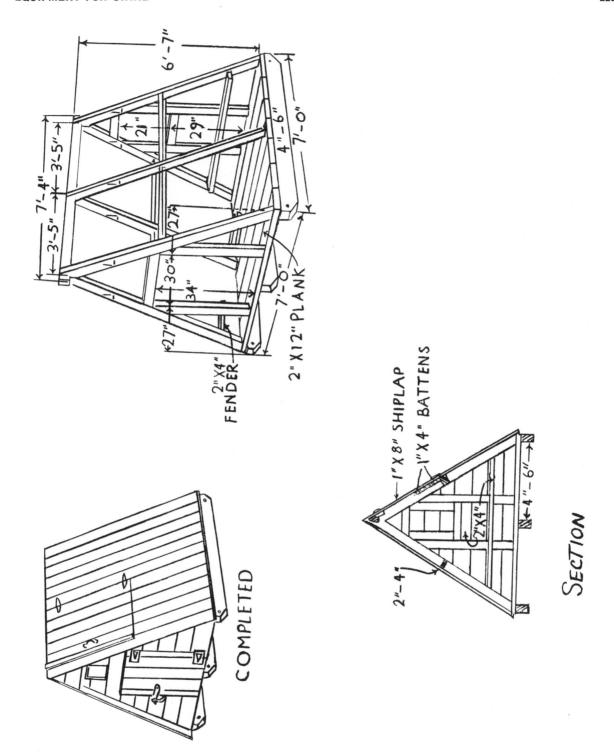

6'-7"

7'-4"

3'-5"

3'-5"

21"

29"

4"-6"

7'-0"

27"

30"

34"

27"

2"X4" FENDER

7'-8"

2"X12" PLANK

1"X8" SHIPLAP

1"X4" BATTENS

2"X4"

2"-4"

4"-6"

SECTION

COMPLETED

A-type hog house.

This type house is economical to construct and has built-in strength through its design.

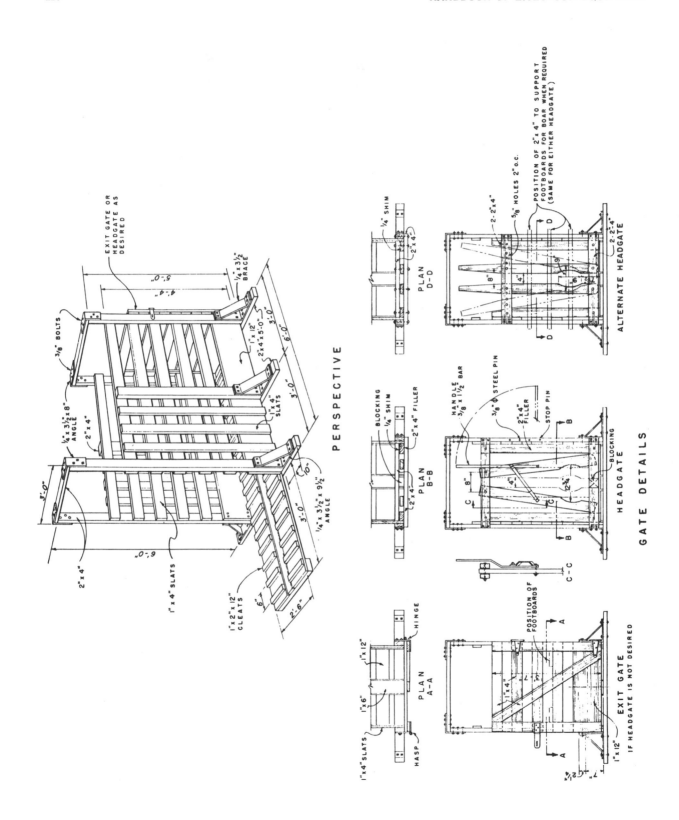

Breeding crate.

Supports boar on two 2" x 6" footboards with front ends resting on cleated gate and rear ends on cleated floor; adjust height to suit, then insert a 2" x 4" bar through slats and under 2" x 6" footboards.

Caution should be used to prevent cracking animal's jaw with headgate. (Oregon State University Cooperative Extension Work, Building Plan 40)

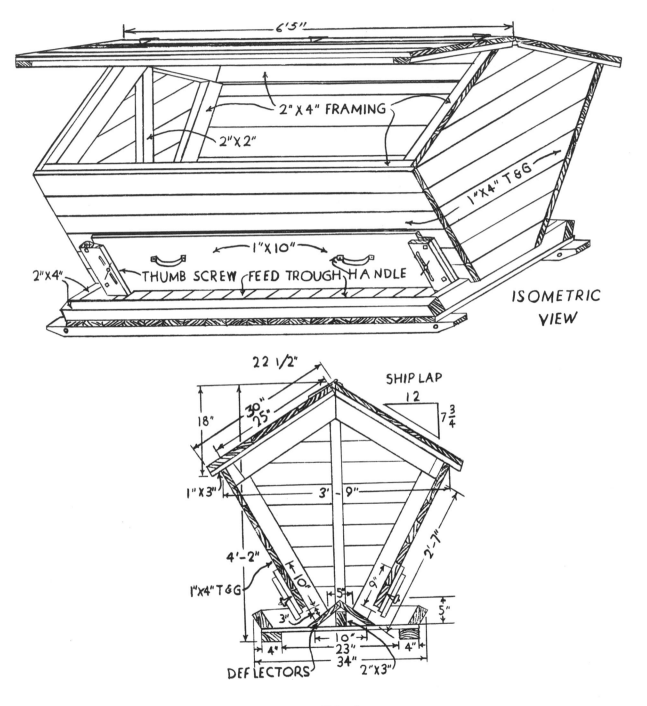

Swine self-feeder.

The use of exterior glue 5/8- or 3/4-inch plywood in most instances will lower cost of construction and increase strength; however, the ends of the feeder especially should be painted whenever plywood is used. (Montana State University)

Chapter XI

EQUIPMENT FOR SHOWS AND EXHIBITIONS

Much of the equipment used for livestock in competitive events, like fairs and shows, is purchased because exhibitors wish to make as professional an appearance as possible. Generally, homemade equipment is not showy or precise enough to match the special grooming and condition of the animal. While some items like tack boxes can be made in the shop, leather goods look better if made by a skilled craftsman. Common hand tools, like brushes, combs, buckets, shovels, pitchforks, etc., also are best purchased. Blankets, electric clippers, and brushes are necessary pieces of equipment, and it is well to make a permanent list to keep inside the tack box so items like these are on hand when needed.

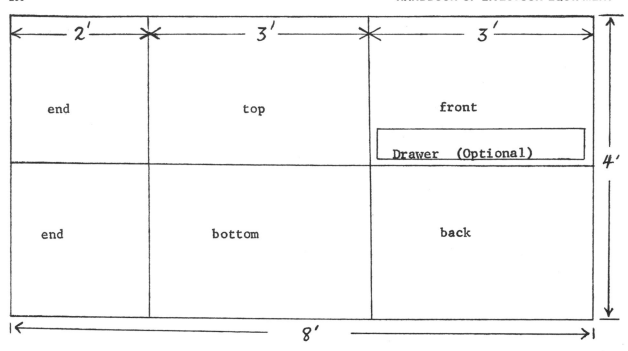

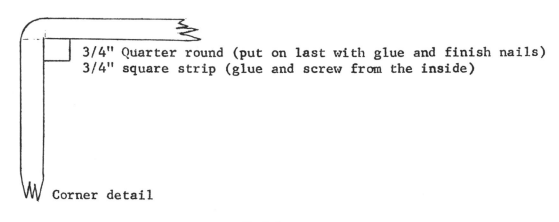

3/4" Quarter round (put on last with glue and finish nails)
3/4" square strip (glue and screw from the inside)

Corner detail

Tack box.

Here is an excellent tack box for Chapter or group use. It is too large for an individual, but can be scaled down to fit one's needs. It may be built with many variations to suit the needs of the individual, such as a sliding box for small gear in top, a drawer in the bottom protected with a false bottom, upright divider clips on top to hold combs, etc. It is a good idea to put runners on the bottom and recessed handles on the ends. Built from 3/4-inch exterior plywood and protected by good paint, it will last a long time, but it is a little on the heavy side. Using 5/8-inch or 1/2-inch plywood lightens it considerably, and it seems solid enough. It is important to use a quality piece of 4 x 8 exterior plywood, and all cuts and measurements must be absolutely square.

Note: All work is done from the inside, with the exception of the bottom, which is put on last. Make sure screws are spaced so the top can be cut off on a table saw without hitting a screw.

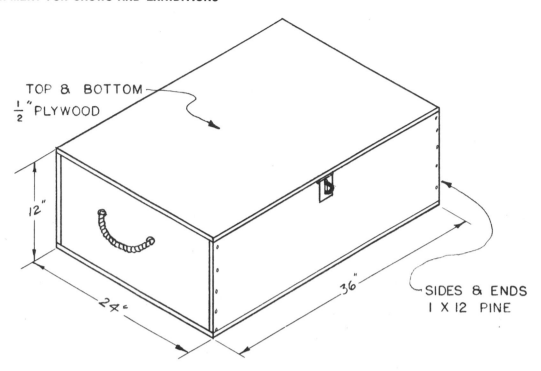

Show box (tack box).

This simple show box for individual use can be made from a few short pieces of 1" x 12" pine lumber and ½-inch plywood. It is inexpensive and strong, and can be carried by one man. Thinner plywood may be used if desired.

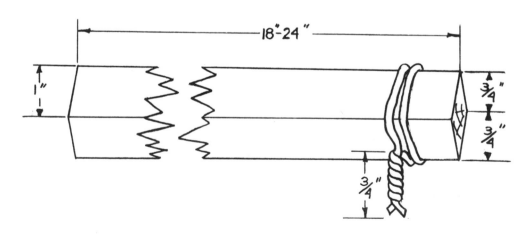

Show stick.

This show stick is easy to make and does the job of moving animals in the show ring very effectively. Start with a 1" x 1" piece of lumber that is free of knots, and work down according to dimensions. The prod is soft iron wire or baling wire twisted on the end and snipped off with a sidecutter plier.

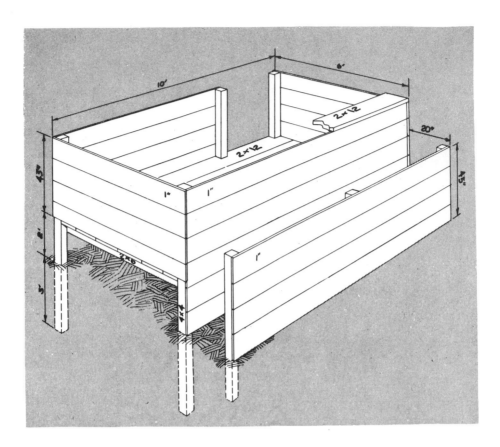

Auction ring plan.

The plan shown calls for a 10-foot entrance alley no less than 24 feet in length. A wide alley permits freedom for single lots, or cows with calves, and also permits the halter cattle to be tied to the alley fence for final coat dressing and changing of halters. The sliding cross stops will save much time on sale day. They should be opened only half way, and stub post guides should be set to protect the free ends.

The sale ring should be made of heavy posts set 6 to 8 feet apart. The corner posts may be set inside the wire, but it is often better to force the wire against the corner posts (set outside) by using a vertical 2 x 4 or 2 x 6 inside the wire and long bolts to draw it up to the corner posts.

Some breeders have found that 2 x 8's placed at the base of the ring help keep the straw in place and are an effective aid in making the cattle look their best if the planks are painted brown.

Often times a calf pen needs to be erected adjacent to the entrance alley, and a gate cut in the last section of the entrance alley so that cow and calf are together as they enter the ring. If preferred, the calf alley can have a separate entrance to the ring. Both ways will work satisfactorily.

A 2 x 4 slide latch will work best on the auction ring gates as it can be opened from either side. (Continued on next page.)

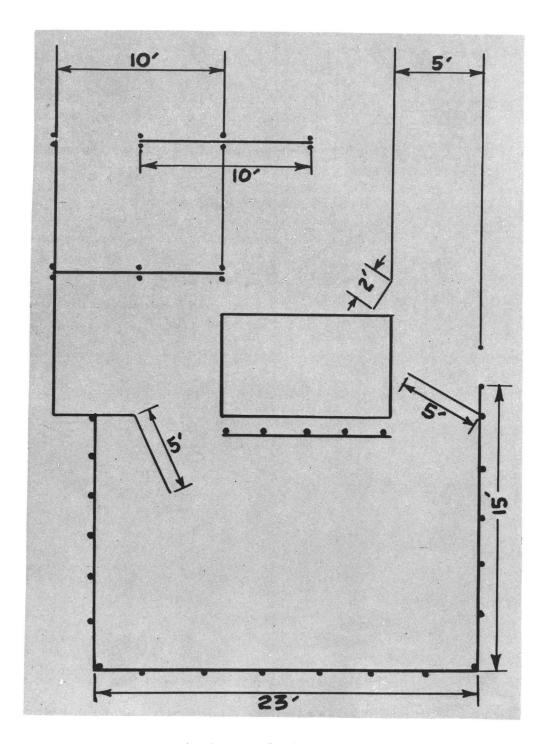

Auction ring plan (continued).

(American Hereford Association)

Chapter XII

HAND TOOLS FOR LIVESTOCK

A considerable number of small tools and other items of equipment are necessary to an efficient livestock operation. Simple tools, like hammers, saws, fence pliers, etc., are essential for everyday use. With a small amount of additional study and effort, anyone mechanically inclined can operate power equipment, including an arc welder and cutting torch. All of these items will speed up repair and save time, especially if broken equipment has to be taken to some distant location to repair. In addition, there are specialized hand tools—those that are difficult to purchase or that meet a specific local or personal standard—that can be fabricated at home or in the shop. Many of these items are handy pieces of equipment that students can make for practice or to enter in a local fair for exhibition purposes.

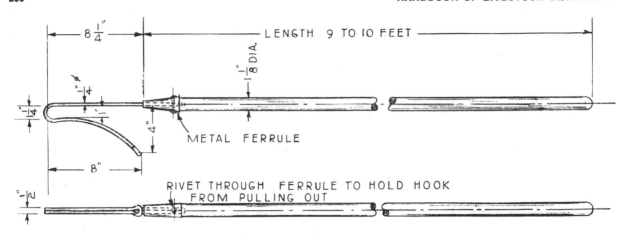

Shepherd's crook.

Every sheepman needs this device to speed up and simplify the task of catching sheep. An old hoe or shovel handle can be adapted to make this equipment.

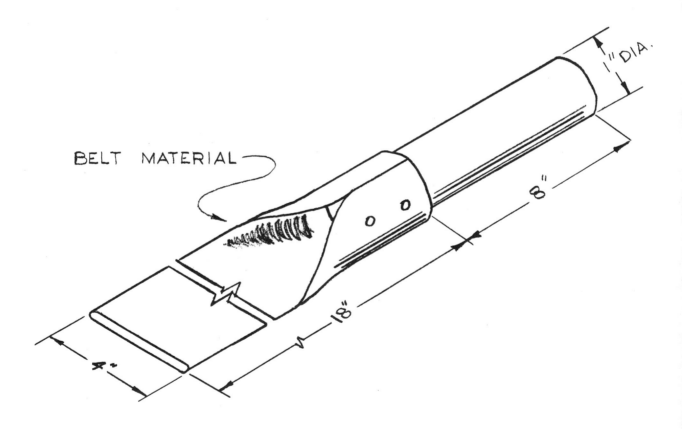

Livestock swat.

An old leather or rubber belt about 1/8- or 3/16-inch thick makes a dandy swat. The belting should be secured to the wooden handle by screws so it does not come loose under constant use.

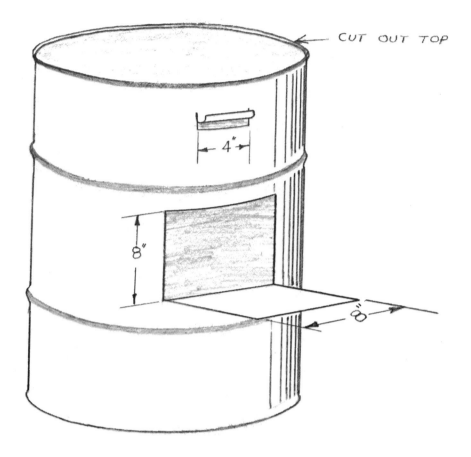

Branding iron heater.

Use a 20- or 30-gallon steel barrel, and with a chisel or cutting torch cut out two rectangular-shaped openings, leaving the flap attached as indicated. On the larger opening, bend the flap down so it sticks out at a 90-degree angle. This provides a platform for the branding irons to lie on and also holds them at the most advantageous spot above the fire. The top flap is bent into a circle to form a handle to carry the heater.

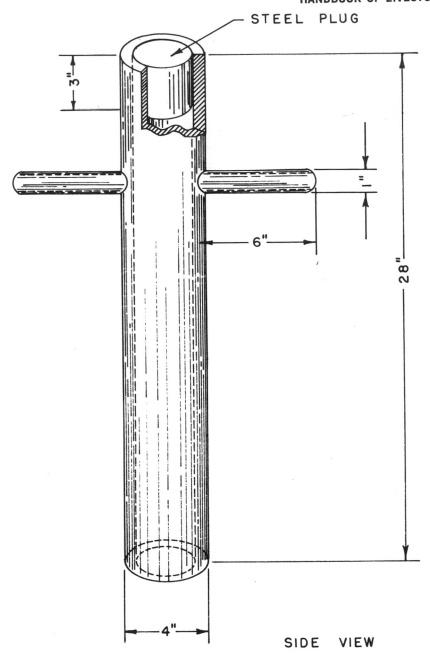

STEEL PLUG

3"

1"

6"

28"

4"

SIDE VIEW

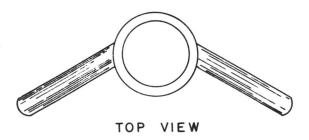

TOP VIEW

Steel post driver.

Construction procedure:
1. Construct a plug by using pipes of smaller sizes, and weld both ends solid.
2. Cut handles to sit at an angle, and weld in place.
3. Weld solid the end which receives the 4-inch plug.
4. Paint with rust-inhibiting paint and finish with an enamel paint.

BILL OF MATERIALS
1—4" x 28" black pipe
2—1" x 6" black pipes for handles
1—4" x 3" plug

Some persons prefer to use 3-inch pipe—or even 2-inch as 4-inch pipe is unwieldy. The plug's diameter will be according to the size of pipe used. If available, single x or double x tubing makes an excellent steel post driver.

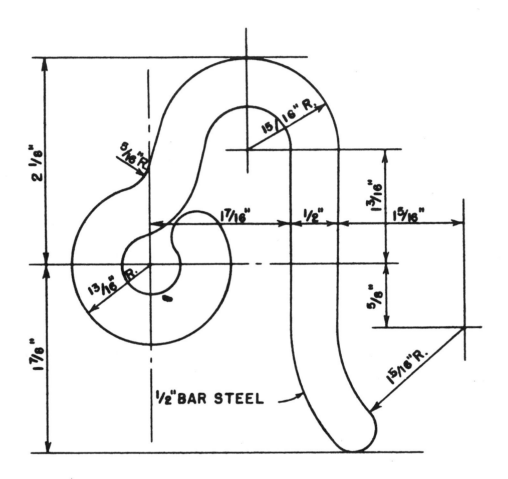

Gate hook.

This is a good practice item for students to make, as it gives experience in measuring, bending, heating, and shaping metal. It is generally fastened to the end of a flexible chain.

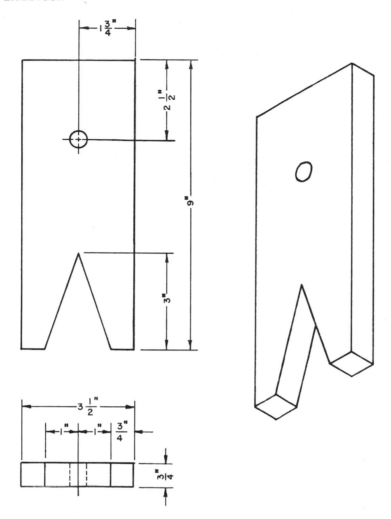

Practice wood block.

One of the first woodworking exercises for students in shop should be a simple, useful practice item such as this bootjack. A block of wood nailed on the underside near the point of the "V" makes it a handy bootjack, especially useful for removing cowboy boots.

BILL OF MATERIALS
1—1 x 4—12" long

Construction Procedure:
1. Dress one edge of block.
2. Mark ends square to length and mark second side to width.
3. Saw off ends with hand saw. DO NOT PLANE.
4. Dress second edge, using plane.
5. Mark out "V" notch.
6. Cut out "V" notch with crosscut hand saw.
7. Mark out hole.
8. Drill hole, using carpenter's brace and No. 8 auger bit.
9. Hand in with papers to be graded.

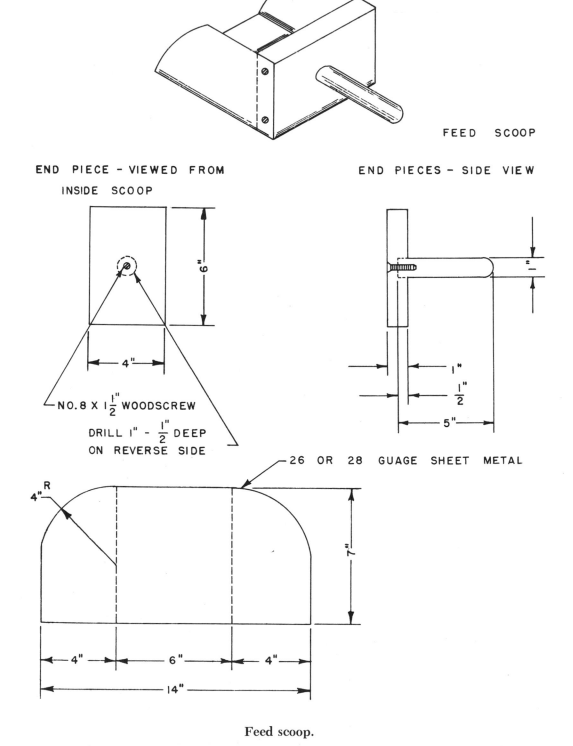

FEED SCOOP

END PIECE - VIEWED FROM
INSIDE SCOOP

END PIECES - SIDE VIEW

6"

4"

NO.8 X 1$\frac{1}{2}$" WOODSCREW

DRILL 1" - $\frac{1}{2}$" DEEP
ON REVERSE SIDE

1"

1"

$\frac{1}{2}$"

5"

26 OR 28 GUAGE SHEET METAL

R
4"

7"

4"   6"   4"

14"

Feed scoop.

This scoop is easy to make and provides a handy sheet metal exercise for beginning students.

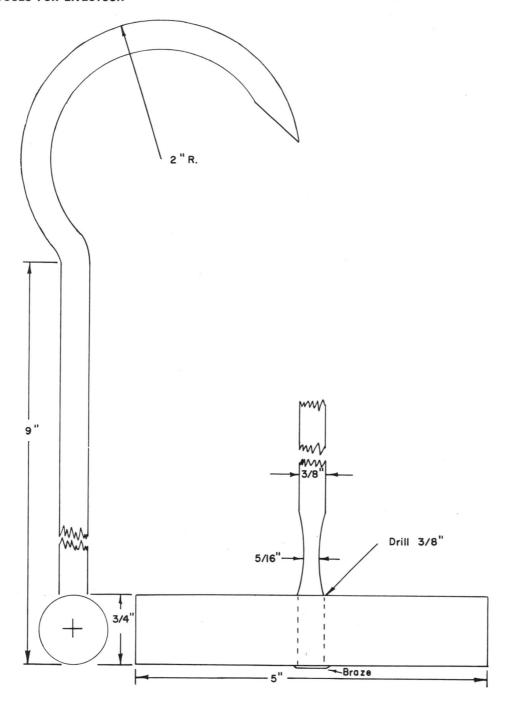

Hay hook.

Hay hooks can be purchased, but many persons prefer to design and make their own, incorporating angles and weight of rod especially suited to their liking.

BILL OF MATERIALS

1—⅜" x 19⅜" tool steel or mild steel case hardened
1—¾" x 5" black pipe

Chapter XIII

STANDARDS AND MEASUREMENTS

In order to function effectively and efficiently, buildings and equipment must be constructed to precise standards. Width of gutters in barns, size of silos for specific herds, inside dimensions of cattle chutes, etc., are but a few examples of the need for exact measurements. For instance, a chute just a few inches too large permits animals to turn around, whereas one a few inches too narrow restricts passage of larger animals.

Since the safety of livestock is involved, standards regarding number of livestock shipped in trucks or cars should be followed carefully to avoid overcrowding. A great deal of experimental work and everyday experience has gone into developing standards for livestock equipment. No particular order is followed in presenting these standards, and occasionally different authorities will vary in their recommendations; however, the variation is slight, and, in general, the standards are in agreement. Whenever a piece of equipment is being constructed, measurements given in plans or in standard tables should be followed carefully.

Volume = diameter x 0.7854 x height (for circular bin)
Volume = length x width x height (for rectangular bin)
Capacity of grain bin in bushels is volume in cubic feet x 0.8
Capacity of corn crib in bushels is volume in cubic feet x 0.4
1 bushel = 1¼ cubic feet
1 cubic foot = 0.8 bushel
1 bushel ear corn = 2½ cubic feet
1 cubic foot ear corn = 0.4 bushel
1 board foot = 1″ x 12″ x 12″ nominal dimensions
1 gallon water = 8.3 pounds
1 cubic foot water = 7.5 gallons
1 gallon water = 231 cubic inches
1 cubic yard concrete = 81 square feet 4-inch floor
1 cubic yard concrete = 54 square feet 6-inch floor
0.43 pound per square inch = column of water 1 foot high
1 pound per square inch = column of water 2.31 feet high

Weights and measures.

1 pound (lb.) = 453.59 grams (gm.)
1 ounce (oz.) = 28.35 grams
1 kilogram (kg. or kilo) = 1,000 grams
1 gram = 1,000 milligrams (mg.)
1 milligram = 1,000 micrograms (mcg.)

1 mcg. per lb. = 2 mg. per ton
1 mg. per lb. = 2 gm. per ton
1 mg. per lb. = 2.2046 parts per million (p.p.m.)
.01 per cent = 90.8 gm. per ton

Weight conversions.

Crop	Lbs./Bu.	Lbs./Cu. Ft.	Freshly Ground	
			Lbs./Bu.	Lbs. Cu. Ft.
Wheat	60	48.0	50	43
Barley	48	38.4	37	28
Oats	32	25.6	23	18
Flax	56	44.8	—	—
Rye	56	44.8	48	38
Corn (shelled)	56	44.8	48	38
Corn (ear)	70	28.0	45	36
Soybeans	60	48.0	—	—
Grain sorghum	56	44.8	—	—

Hay-Straw	Loose Ft./Ton	Lb./Cu.Ft.	Baled Ft./Ton	Lb./Cu.Ft.	Chopped Cut	Ft./Ton	Lb./Cu.Ft.
Alfalfa	450-500	4.4-4	200-330	10-6	1½''	285-360	7-5.5
Non-legume	450-600	4.4-3.3	250-330	8-6	3''	300-400	6.7-5
Straw	670-1000	3-2	400-500	5-4		250-350	8-5.7

Crop weights (approximate).

Floor Length	450 Lbs.	600 Lbs.	800 Lbs.	1000 Lbs.	1200 Lbs.	1400 Lbs.
8 ft.	8	7	5	4	4	3
10 ft.	10	8	7	6	5	4
12 ft.	13	10	8	7	6	5
15 ft.	16	13	10	9	8	7
18 ft.	20	16	13	11	9	8
20 ft.	22	18	14	12	10	9
24 ft.	27	22	17	15	13	11
28 ft.	31	25	20	17	15	13
30 ft.	34	27	22	19	16	14
32 ft.	36	29	23	20	17	15
36 ft.	41	33	26	22	19	17
42 ft.	48	39	31	28	22	20

Maximum loading for cattle.

(Livestock Conservation, Inc.)

Animal	Condition	Floor or Bedded Area
		(sq. ft.)
Breeding cow	With or without calf	50
Calf	Feeders, stockers, replacement heifers	30
Yearling	Feeders, stockers, replacement heifers	40
Fattening stock	Average 750 pounds for fattening period	45
Fattening stock	Average 950 pounds for fattening period	50
Cow	In maternity pen	120
Calf	2 or more in pen	20

Floor areas for cattle, with access
to outside yards or pasture.

Equipment	Conditions	Inside Width
		(ft.)
Feed bunk for grain or silage	Feed from both sides	3 to 3½
	Feed from one side	2½
Portable hay bunk	Feed from sides and ends	6
Hay manger, permanent	Feed from one side	2½
	Feed from two sides	3½

Floor of hay mangers or bunks should be as near ground level as practical.
Trough height for fattening mature stock: 30 inches to lip, 24 inches for calves.
Trough length for mature animals: 28 inches to 30 inches; 20 inches for calves.
Self-feeder trough length: 9 inches per head.
For free choice of silage allow space for 65 per cent to 75 per cent of animals,
and hay space, when feeding silage and hay free choice, 25 per cent to 35 per
cent of animals. If feed is not on free choice allow feed space for all animals to
eat at same time.

Recommended dimensions for cattle-feeding equipment.

Breed	Average Weight	Average Width	Average Length
Holstein	1300	3'9"	5'2"
Brown Swiss	1350	3'10"	5'2"
Guernsey	1100	3'6"	4'10"
Jersey	1100	3'6"	4'8"

Stall sizes for dairy cattle.

Self-feeders ....1 inch per animal
Hay and grain..15 inches to 18 inches per ewe
Hay and grain..12 inches per lamb
Lambing pen...12 to 16 square feet per ewe
Space under shelter...10 to 15 square feet per ewe

Feed space required for sheep.

	Barn or Shed	Feed Lot		Hay Rack		Feed Trough		Self-feeder	Water
	Per Animal	Dirt	Paved	Length	Width	Length	Width	Length	Per Day
	(sq. ft.)	(sq. ft.)	(sq. ft.)	(in.)	(in.)	(in.)	(in.)	(in.)	(gals.)
Dry ewes	12-20	25-40	20-30	18-24	14-16	16-22	14-16		1½
Ewes with lambs	15-22	25-50	25-40	18-24	14-16	16-22	14-16		2
Stud rams	20-30	30-60	30-60	18-24	14-16	20-24	14-16		2
Feeder lambs	10-12	20-30	10-20	12-15	12-14	12-15	14-16	3 lambs for each 12'' feeder space	½

Recommended space for sheep.

Size of Hog	Dimension of Crate		
Weight	Length	Height	Width
(lbs.)	(ft.-in.)	(in.)	(in.)
50	3-3	23	12
100	3-6	24	14
150	3-8	28	15
200	4-2	30	16
250	4-6	33	17
300	5-0	34	18
400	5-4	36	20
500	5-8	37	21
600	6-0	38	22

Size of crates for different size hogs.

Feed	Unit	Weight	Volume
		(lbs.)	*(cu. ft.)*
Shelled corn	bu.	56	1.25
Ear corn	bu.	70	2.50
Oats	bu.	32	1.25
Wheat	bu.	60	1.25
Barley	bu.	48	1.25
Sacked feed	cu. ft.	40 (estimated)	
Fresh ground feed	cu. ft.	25 (estimated)	
Silage (in trench or bunker silo)	cu. ft.	30-35	
Silage (upright silo)	cu. ft.	30-50	
Silage (loose removed from silo)	cu. ft.	18 (approximate)	
Hay (long)	ton		500
Hay (chopped, long)	ton		250-300
Hay (baled, loose)	ton		200-220
Hay (bales, tight)	ton		80-100

Weight and volume of stored feed and capacity of storages.

Area Needed

Alfalfa...485 cubic feet per ton
Timothy ....640 cubic feet per ton
Clover..510 cubic feet per ton
Chopped hay...225 cubic feet per ton
Baled hay (closely stacked).......................................150 to 200 cubic feet per ton
Straw (loose) ....1,000 cubic feet per ton
Straw (baled) ....200 cubic feet per ton
Sawdust and shavings...165 to 230 cubic feet per ton
Silage..35 to 70 cubic feet per ton
Concentrate ....40 to 70 cubic feet per ton

Feed and bedding storage.

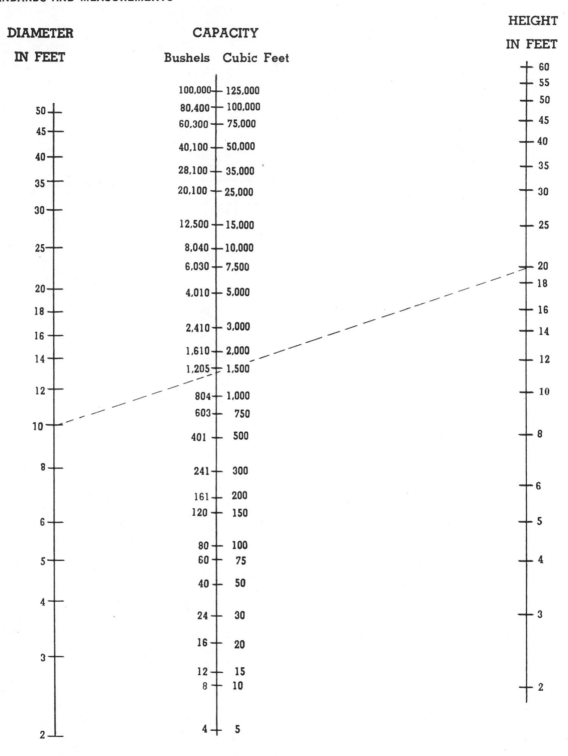

Capacities of round bins.

Lay a rule from the "diameter" line to the "height in feet" line. When it crosses the center line, read bushels or cubic feet as desired.

No. Cows	Tons Silage Needed for 180 Days' Feeding[1]	Size of Silo Necessary			
		Depth	Width Bottom	Width Top	Length
	(tons)	(ft.)	(ft.)	(ft.)	(ft.)
10	36	6	8	10	39
12	43	6	8	10	46
15	54	6	8	12	52
20	72	8	9	12	49
25	90	8	9	12	62
30	108	8	9	13	71
35	126	10	10	14	60
40	144	10	10	14	69
45	162	10	10	14	78

1. Feeding at rate of 40 pounds per day.

Capacity of trench silos.

Depth A	Top Width B	Bottom Width C	Approximate Number of Tons per Running Foot
(ft.)	(ft.)	(ft.)	(tons)
10	11	6	1.5
10	15	8	2.0
10	18	10	2.5
8	10	6	1.1
8	12	7	1.3
8	15	8	1.6
6	9	6	0.8
6	11	7	0.9
6	13	8	1.1

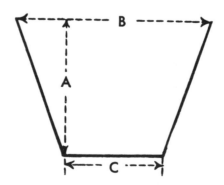

Capacities for horizontal silos.

(DHIA Herd Record Book)

Type of Animal	Air Flow per Unit	Basis for Unit
Dairy	100 CFM	1,000-pound cow
Swine..............................	15 CFM	100 pounds of pork
Poultry	3 CFM	1 hen

Amount of air flow needed in cubic feet of air per minute (CFM).

(University of Minnesota Extension Service Bulletin 253)

1 gal. = 8.34 lbs. = 231 cu. in. = 0.1337 cu. ft.
1 cu. ft. = 7.4805 gal.= 62.4 lbs.
1 acre in. = 27,154 gal. = 3,360 cu. ft.
1 acre ft. = 325,850 gal. = 43,560 cu. ft.
1 cu. ft. per sec. = 448.8 gal. per min. = 0.9917 acre in. per H.
Feet Head x .433 = lbs. per sq. in.
100 gal. per min. = 1 acre in. per 4½ hrs. = 5.3 acre in. per 24 hrs.
1 horsepower = 550 ft. lbs. per sec. = 33,000 ft. lbs. per min. = 746 watts

Water.

To compute cubic feet in a mow multiply length by width by height (all in feet).
The USDA recommends the following rules for estimating cubic feet in stacks. (Leaflet No. 72, USDA)
For low, round-topped rectangular stacks:

$$[(0.52 \times O) - (0.44 \times W)] \times W \times L$$

For high, round-topped rectangular stacks:

$$[(0.52 \times O) - (0.46 \times W)] \times W \times L$$

For square, flat-topped rectangular stacks:

$$[(0.56 \times O) - (0.55 \times W)] \times W \times L$$

For round stacks:

$$(0.04 \times O) - (0.012 \times C) \times C^2$$

In these formulas O is the "over" (the distance from the base on one side of the stack, over the stack, and to the base on the other side); W is the width; L is the length; and C is the circumference of a round stack, or the distance around it. In measuring a round stack, the "over" should be an average of two measurements made at right angles to each other.

Another method often used for estimating the volume of a stack consists of multiplying the length by the width by the "over" (all in feet), multiplying by 3, and then dividing by 10.

Measurement of mows and stacks.

To determine approximate number of tons, divide the number of the cubic feet in the mow or stack by the cubic feet in a ton.

Although many factors affect the density of hay, the averages as given in the following table can be used with fairly good results.

Tons of hay in mow or stacks.

USDA Leaflet #72

Kind of Hay	Length of Time in Stack	
	30 to 90 Days	Over 90 Days
Timothy	640 cu. ft.	625 cu. ft.
Clover-Timothy	580 cu. ft.	515 cu. ft.
Wild	600 cu. ft.	450 cu. ft.
Alfalfa	485 cu. ft.	470 cu. ft.
Chopped Alfalfa (Cut ⅜ in. lengths)		150 cu. ft.
Chopped Alfalfa (Cut ½ in. lengths)		260 cu. ft.
Chopped Alfalfa (Cut 1 in. lengths)		300 cu. ft.
Chopped Alfalfa (Cut 2 in. lengths)		370 cu. ft.

Cubic feet per ton of hay.

1 centare (ca.) = 1 square meter
1 are (a.) = 100 sq. m.
1 hectare (ha.) = 10,000 sq. m. = 2.47104 A.
1 labor (lah-bore) = 177 1/7 A.
1 square league = 25 labors = 4,409 A.
1 sq. in. = 6.451626 sq. cm.
1 sq. ft. = 144 sq. in.
1 sq. yd. = 9 sq. ft.
1 sq. rd. = 1 perch = 30¼ sq. yd. = 272¼ sq. ft.
1 acre (A.) = 160 sq. rd. = 4,840 sq. yd. = 43,560 sq. ft. = 0.404687 ha.
1 sq. mi. = 1 section = 640 A.
1 township = 36 sections = 23,040 A.

Area.

1 cubic centimeter (cc.) = 0.061023 cu. in.
1 cubic decimeter = 1,000 cc. = 61.0234 cu. in.
1 cubic meter = 1,000,000 cc. = 35.31445 cu. ft.
1 cu. in. = 16.387162 cc.
1 cu. ft. = 1,728 cu. in. = 28,317.016 cc.
1 cu. yd. = 27 cu. ft. = 46,656 cu. in.

Volume.

1 gill = 118.292 ml.
1 pt. = 4 gi. = 473.167 ml. = 0.473167 *l.*
1 qt. = 2 pt. = 8 gi. = 0.946333 *l.*
1 gal. = 4 qt. = 8 pt. = 3.785332 *l.* = 231 cu. in.
31½ gal. = 1 barrel
2 barrels = 1 hogshead
1 liter (l.) = 1,000 milliliters (ml. or cc.) = 2.11342 pt. = 1.05671 qt.
1 teaspoon = 4.93 ml.
3 teaspoons = 1 tablespoon = 14.79 ml.
2 tablespoons = 1 fluid oz. = 29.578 ml.
16 tablespoons = 8 fluid oz. = 1 cup = 236.583 ml.
2 cups = 16 fluid oz. = 1 pt. = 473.167 ml.

Capacity (liquid measure).

1 liter = 61.025 cu. in. = 0.908102 dry qt.
1 dekaliter (dkl.) = 10 *l.* = 0.28378 bu.
1 hecktoliter (hl.) = 100 *l.* = 2.8378 bu.
1 dry pt. = 33.60031 cu. in. = 0.550599 *l.*
1 dry qt. = 2 dry pt. = 1.101198 *l.*
1 peck = 8 dry qt. = 8.80958 *l.*
1 bushel = 4 pk. = 32 dry qt. = 35.2383 *l.*
1 Winchester (U.S.) bu. = 1.244 cu. ft. = 2,150.42 cu. in.
1 Imperial (British) bu. = 2,219.36 cu. in. = 1.0305 Winchester bu.

Capacity (dry measure).

Item	Gallons Needed in 24 Hrs.
Each person	50
Each dry cow or beef animal	12
Each milking cow	30
Each hog	4
Each sheep	2
Each 100 chickens	5
Washing dairy utensils	50

Your well and pump should be able to supply about half of the daily requirement in one hour. This rate of supply will usually insure adequate pressure even at periods of peak demands.

How to estimate water needs.

The unit of measure is the board foot, which is a board one inch thick and one foot square. Lumber is always sold on the basis of 1,000 feet board measure. (B.M.) *Formula:* To find B.M. multiply length in feet by width in feet by thickness in inches.

Board measure.

24 grains = 1 pwt.
20 pwts. = 1 ounce = 31.103 gm.
12 ounces = 1 pound = 373 gm.

Troy weight.

20 grains = 1 scruple = 1.296 grams
3 scruples = 1 dram
8 drams = 1 ounce = 31.103 gm.
12 ounces = 1 pound = 373 gm.

Apothecaries' weight.

1 microgram (gm.) = 0.000001 gm.
1 milligram (mgm.) = 0.001 gm.
1 gram (gm.) = 1,000 mg. = 15.4324 grains
1 kilogram (kgm.) = 1,000 gm. = 2.2046 lb.
1 metric ton = 1,000 kg. = 2,204.62 lb.

Metric weight.

1 grain (gr.) = 64.79891 mgm.
1 ounce (oz.) = 437.5 gr. = 28.34953 gm.
1 pound (lb.) = 16 oz. = 7,000 gr. = 453.5924 gm.
1 short hundredweight = 100 lb.
1 long hundredweight = 112 lb.
1 short ton = 2,000 lb.
1 long ton = 2,240 lb.

Avoirdupois weights.

1 kilometer(km.) = 1,000 m. = 0.62137 mile
1 meter (m.) = 1 m. = 39.37 in. = 3.28 ft.
1 centimeter (cm.) = 1/100 m. = 0.3937 in.
1 millimeter (mm.) = 1/1000 m. = 0.03937 in.
1 micron = 1/1000 mm.
1 millimicron = 1/1000 micron
1 mile = 5,280 ft. = 1,760 yd. = 320 rd. = 80 chains
1 chain = 66 ft. = 22 yd. = 4 rd. = 100 links
1 rod = 16½ ft. = 5½ yd. = 25 links
1 yard = 3 ft. = 36 in. = 0.9144 m.
1 foot = 12 in. = 30.48006 cm.
1 link = 7.92 in.
1 inch = 2.54005 cm. = 25.4 mm.

Length.

60 seconds = 1 minute
60 minutes = 1 degree
360 degrees = 1 circle

Circular measure.

Use of Concrete[1]	U.S. Gal. of Water per Sack Cement with Average Moist Sand	Aggregates per Sack Cement		Largest Size of Aggregate	Sacks of Cement Needed for 1 Cu. Yd. of Mixed Concrete
		Sand Cu. Ft.	Gravel Cu. Ft.		
Most farm construction such as floors, steps, basement, walls, walks, yard pavements, silos, grain bins, water tanks, etc.	5	2¼	3	1½ in.	6¼
Concrete in thick sections and not subject to freezing. Thick footings, thick foundations, retaining walls, engine bases.	5½	2¾	4	1½ in.	5
Thin reinforced concrete such as milk cooling tanks, fence posts, thin floors, most uses where concrete is 2 in. to 4 in. thick.	5	2¼	2½	¾ in.	6½
Very thin concrete such as top course of 2-course floors and pavements, concrete lawn furniture, most uses where concrete is 1 in. to 2 in. thick.	4	1¾	2¼	⅜ in.	8

1. "Plans for Concrete Farm Building," Portland Cement Association.

Suggested concrete mixes.

Content[1]	Flat Work (using 1½-in. max. size aggregate)			Formed Work (using ½-in. max. size aggregate)		
	Severe Exposure	Normal Exposure	Mild Exposure	Severe Exposure	Normal Exposure	Mild Exposure
	Garbage feeding floors, floors in dairy plants	Paved barnyards, floors for farm buildings, sidewalks	Footings, concrete improvements in mild climates	Mangers for silage feeding, manure pits	Reinforced concrete walls, beams, tanks, foundations	Concrete improvements in mild climates
Cement content: minimum number of sacks per cu. yd. of concrete	7	6	5	7¾	6½	5½
Water content (includes that contained in aggregates): maximum gals. per sack of cement	5	6	7	5	6	7

1. "Ready-Mixed Concrete for the Farm," Portland Cement Association.

Guide for ordering ready-mixed concrete.

Weight of Cow (lbs.)	Stall Length[1]	Stall Width
800	4'6"	3'6"
1,000	4'9"	3'9"
1,200	5'0"	4'0"
1,400	5'4"	4'4"
1,600	5'8"	4'8"

1. Stall lengths may need to be increased 2 to 6 inches when tie stalls or electric cow trainers are used.

Recommended minimum dimensions for stanchion stalls.

(USDA Bulletin #123)

1,300- to 1,500-lb. cow—4'0" to 4'6"
1,000- to 1,200-lb. cow—3'8" to 4'0"
800- to 1,000-lb. cow—3'4" to 3'8"

Stall width.

The maximum stalls per row should not exceed 25, with two rows per exit. Alleys should be paved and pitched toward the exit or the manure handling area.

20 stalls (2 rows of 10)—Minimum alley width 8'0"
30 stalls (2 rows of 15)—Minimum alley width 10'0"
40 stalls (2 rows of 20)—Minimum alley width 12'0"
50 stalls (2 rows of 25)—Minimum alley width 14'0"

Alley width.

	Cu. Ft. per Head per Hour
Horses	4,924
Cows	3,953
Hogs	1,510
Sheep	929

Rate of supply of air to barns to provide pure air for classes of livestock.

	Head
Horses—1 sq. ft. cross-sectional area for	5
Cattle —1 sq. ft. cross-sectional area for	6
Hogs —1 sq. ft. cross-sectional area for	18
Sheep —1 sq. ft. cross-sectional area for	24

Amount of out-take flues required to keep air in buildings sufficiently pure for livestock.

INDEX

Trench silo, 50
Trough, 200, 203, 223
Twitch, ring, 166, 167
    temporary, 167
Types of barns, 24

W

Wallow, 215
Water trough, 56
    cattle, 58
    hog, 223

Waterer
    heated, 54, 55
    swine, 216
Watering equipment, 29
Weighing crate, 206
Windbreaks, 2
Wire bender, 98
Wire fences, 72, 80
Wire splicer, 98
Wing gate, 133
Wood fence, 81, 82
Wool-packing rack, 201